THE TIME WAS 1943. The great battles of World War II still raged on every front. Count Col. Claus von Stauffenberg, member of the German General Staff, was rushed back from Africa—an authentic hero—one eye and one hand gone, a body ruined beyond repair. Von Stauffenberg had served his country well—in the Rhineland, in Czechoslovakia, Austria, Poland, Russia and finally in North Africa.

Lying in a hospital bed in Munich, he reviews the events that brought him there. Slowly the conviction grows that loyalty to mankind and to Germany takes precedence over his oath of allegiance to his superiors and to the man who is the author of all the horror and destruction that is engulfing the world—Adolf Hitler.

After months of convalescing from near fatal wounds, he pushes aside hopes of rejoining his wife and family, and accepts a post on the staff of General Olbricht, a secret anti-Nazi, firmly committed to the proposition that Adolf Hitler and the Nazi party must be destroyed. On the surface, he remains the relaxed and confident general staff officer, efficiently organizing the supply of men and material for the front. Secretly he becomes the driving force and coordinator of the plot to organize the army and as many civilian dissenters as possible to eliminate Hitler and the Nazi regime and set up a new government dedicated to peace and reconciliation.

Under cover of *Valkyrie,* the code name of the master plan for organizing the reserves to counter any possible uprisings by slave laborers, the conspiracy matures until it includes plans for the arrest or assassination of Hitler, a nationwide command structure, specific orders for army units, and intricate communication signals with officers in outlying areas. After the failure of several ingenious assassination attempts, von Stauffenberg decides to make the final effort himself. Despite his wounds and physical handicaps, he will meet with Hitler and his officers in a secluded bunker and set off the charge that will free Germany and the world.

CODE NAME VALKYRIE is the narrative of the man and events that led to July 20, 1944, the day a bomb blast shook the Third Reich to its foundations and almost ended the Hitler regime.

CODE NAME VALKYRIE

by JAMES FORMAN

CODE
NAME
VALKYRIE

Count von Stauffenberg and

the Plot to Kill Hitler

S. G. PHILLIPS 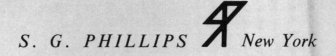 *New York*

LIBRARY OF CONGRESS CATALOGING IN PUBLICATION DATA

Forman, James D.
　Code name Valkyrie.

　SUMMARY: A biography of the German general who
organized the elaborate but ill-fated plot to assas-
sinate Hitler and end the Second World War.
　Bibliography: p.
　1. Schenk von Stauffenberg, Klaus Philipp, Graf,
1907-1944—Juvenile literature. 2. Hitler, Adolf,
1889-1945—Assassination attempt, July 20, 1944—
Juvenile literature. [1. Schenk von Stauffenberg,
Klaus Philipp, Graf, 1907-1944. 2. Hitler, Adolph,
1889-1945—Assassination attempt, July 20, 1944.]
I. Title.

DD256.3.F6　943.086'092'4 [B]　72-12581
ISBN 0-87599-188-2

For the only artists, blood,
bone, heart and soul that I have known;
Alexandra Hunt and Joan Warden,
with abiding love

CONTENTS

ILLUSTRATIONS

MAPS

Illustrations on the following pages were reproduced from captured German Leica filmstrips, provided by the National Archives, Washington, D.C. Photograph numbers are included for identification.

Pp. 23 (#242-HL-7236-30); 133 (#242-PA-196); 163 (#208-AA-207E-1); 168 (#242-HL-7233-21); 189 (#242-HL-7217-14); 229 (#242-X-1); 231 (#242-HL-7235-4); 234 (#242-JRB-50-19); 238 (#131-NO-3-22);

Illustrations on the remaining pages, except for the maps, were provided by the German Information Center, New York, New York. The maps on pages 52, 63, 84 and 154 were drawn by Donald Pitcher.

SOME OF THE PEOPLE INVOLVED

THE CONSPIRATORS

THE ARMY:

BECK, GENERAL LUDWIG
Retired; former Chief of the German General Staff

BUSSCHE, CAPTAIN AXEL VON DEM
Officer in the Infantry

CANARIS, ADMIRAL WILHELM
Chief of the Abwehr *(Bureau of Intelligence)*

FELLGIEBEL, GENERAL ERICH
Chief of Signals, Armed Forces High Command (OKW)

HAEFTEN, LIEUTENANT WERNER VON
Adjutant to Lieutenant Colonel von Stauffenberg

HELLDORF, SS GENERAL COUNT WOLF VON
Chief of Berlin Police

HOEPNER, GENERAL ERICH
Tank commander, later retired by Hitler

KLEIST, LIEUTENANT EWALD HEINRICH VON
Officer in the infantry

MERTZ VON QUIRNHEIM, COLONEL ALBRECHT
Chief of Staff to General Olbricht, General Army Office, Berlin

OLBRICHT, GENERAL FRIEDRICH
Chief of the General Army Office

ROMMEL, FIELD MARSHAL ERWIN
Commander of the Italo-German forces in North Africa, later commander of Army Group B, Western Europe

SCHLABRENDORFF, MAJOR FABIAN VON
Aide to General von Tresckow

STAUFFENBERG, LIEUTENANT COLONEL CLAUS PHILIPP MARIA SCHENK, COUNT VON
Lieutenant Colonel in the Army

STIEFF, GENERAL HELMUTH
Chief of Organization Branch, Army High Command (OKH)

STUELPNAGEL, GENERAL KARL HEINRICH VON
Military Governor of France

TRESCKOW, MAJOR GENERAL HENNING VON
Chief of Staff to the Commander, Army Group Center, Russian front

WITZLEBEN, FIELD MARSHAL ERWIN VON
Commander in Chief in Western Europe, later retired

THE CIVILIANS:

BONHOEFFER, PASTOR DIETRICH
Theologian

GOERDELER, CARL
Former Mayor of Leipzig

GISEVIUS, HANS BERND
Police Officer

LEBER, JULIUS
Trade union leader

MOLTKE, HELMUTH, COUNT VON
Legal Advisor to the Abwehr *(Bureau of Intelligence)*

STRUENCK, THEODOR AND ELISABETH

HITLER'S CIRCLE

BORMANN, MARTIN
Deputy Fuehrer of the Nazi Party

DOENITZ, ADMIRAL KARL
Commander in Chief of the Navy

GOEBBELS, JOSEF
Propaganda Minister

GOERING, REICH MARSHAL HERMANN
Commander in Chief of the Air Force

HIMMLER, SS FUEHRER HEINRICH
Chief of the German Police

JODL, GENERAL ALFRED
Chief of Operations, High Command of the Armed Forces (OKW)

KEITEL, FIELD MARSHAL WILHELM
Chief of High Command of the Armed Forces (OKW)

MUSSOLINI, BENITO
Dictator of Italy (Il Duce)

RIBBENTROP, JOACHIM
Foreign Minister

UNCOMMITTED

FROMM, GENERAL FRIEDRICH
Commander of the Home Army, Berlin

GUDERIAN, GENERAL HEINZ
Chief of the Army General Staff after July, 1944

HEUSINGER, GENERAL ADOLF
Chief of Operations, Army High Command

KLUGE, FIELD MARSHAL GUENTHER HANS VON
   Commander, Army Group Center in Eastern Europe; later Commander in Chief, Western Europe and Commander, Army Group B in Western Europe

MANSTEIN, FIELD MARSHAL FRITZ ERICH VON
RUNDSTEDT, FIELD MARSHAL GERD VON
   Leader of Army Group South in Russia, later Commander in Chief, Western Europe (before and after Kluge)

ZEITZLER, LIEUTENANT GENERAL KURT
   Chief of the General Staff

OTHERS

BAMM, SERGEANT WOLFGANG
   Driver for Stauffenberg in North Africa

GEORGE, STEFAN
   Poet and teacher of Stauffenberg

HERBER, LIEUTENANT COLONEL FRANZ
   Stauffenberg's lieutenant in Russia

MEICHSSNER, COLONEL JOACHIM
   On the Operations Staff, Army High Command

STAUFFENBERG, COUNT BERTHOLD VON
   Older brother of Claus von Stauffenberg

STAUFFENBERG, COUNTESS NINA VON
   Wife of Claus von Stauffenberg

BEFORE

IN 1918 Germany lost the First World War. The German Emperor fled, and the old imperial government crumbled amidst starvation and political chaos. In its place a new government, the Weimar Republic, arose to undertake the thankless task of dealing with the victorious Allies. Peace, represented by the Versailles Treaty, was accomplished by a demand for enormous reparations which Germany was totally unable to fulfill. Defeat, in turn, brought shock, humiliation and the myth that her armies had not been vanquished but stabbed in the back by politicians at home.

Born in defeat, indecisive and inexperienced, the young republic was pushed and pulled from right and left, the scapegoat for every dissatisfaction and the whipping boy for political extremists. Prominent among those militant groups was the fascistic party whose members called themselves National Socialists, or Nazis. Their leader was a self-educated Austrian fanatic named Adolf Hitler.

Having failed to overthrow the government in 1923 by force of arms, Hitler resigned himself to political means and to waiting out the era of prosperity that followed the turbulent postwar years. His course was aided by some industrialists and landowners who saw in the young demagogue—he was still in his thirties —a means of furthering their own ends. But it was not until the world-wide depression of 1929, and its resulting miseries, that

Nazism changed from a lunatic fringe ideology into a mass movement.

Amid widespread hunger, discontent and unemployment, Hitler set about capturing votes for his National Socialist German Workers' Party. In his speeches he offered all things to all Germans: reactivating industry, restoring the Army, providing security for the little man and a national purpose for the young. For all, he provided common enemies: the long hated Versailles Treaty, the Allies who fostered it, the Weimar liberals and the Jews, whom he characterized as an inferior race.

The opening of the 1930's saw the German people increasingly polarized between the parties of the extreme right and left. The moderate center, mainstay of the Weimar Republic, collapsed, paralyzed by its inability to unite in the face of a common enemy. Governments rose and fell, shot through with intrigue, unable to provide leadership in the chaos or to control the Nazi gangs sent out to terrorize the opposition. Finally, on January 30, 1933, Field Marshal von Hindenburg, Germany's aging President and onetime commander of the Army, appointed Hitler Chancellor of Germany. The Weimar Republic was ended. The Nazis had come to power.

At first, Hitler was thought by most Germans to be doing a necessary job, cleaning up the chaos of the last few years. He did bring order. He also brought the promise of world prestige and prosperity—but at a price in freedom and humanity which most Germans managed to overlook until it was too late.

At the time, no group apparently stood to gain more than the Army, reduced to a small hard core of officers by the Versailles Treaty and led by a military elite, largely Prussian, left over from World War I. The officers made up an exclusive club, drawn from the landed German nobility—men whose ancestors had extended German power from the Rhine to the Baltic, who had beaten Napoleon, united Germany by blood and iron, and crowned a German Emperor in the traditional home of the Kings of France. Hitler, the onetime corporal, the coarse foreigner, could never be popular with these aristocrats. If they owed loyalty anywhere, it was to their departed Emperor or to their personal ambitions, now thwarted by the Versailles Treaty. But Hitler promised to restore the Army to its former greatness, and when he became Chancellor, many of the young officers were delighted. Even the older generals could lay aside their misgivings by saying, "All that has happened is that he's been given a job," and by remembering that it had been one of their own caste who had raised him to power.

Although the Versailles Treaty banned the German General Staff, a shadow staff existed under the leadership of General Ludwig Beck. Born in 1880, the son of a Protestant Rhinelander, Beck had been a major in World War I. A better administrator than warrior, he rose rapidly in the peacetime Army, and when Hitler seemingly restored the General Staff to its former commanding status, Beck remained at its head. Though never a Nazi, General Beck first achieved notoriety in 1930, when he defended two officers arrested for distributing Nazi propaganda. His only motive was to prevent civilian interference with the men under his command, but the action seemed to place him in the inner circle of the Nazi movement. This illusion vanished as soon as Hitler clarified his international aims.

As early as 1931, over tea and cakes, Hitler had discussed the possibility of a war of revenge—without generals if need be. For the most part, his ideas were regarded as a flight of fancy. Many of the generals opposed war—some because Germany was militarily unprepared, others, including Beck, for political and philosophical reasons. Beck believed that a renewal of world-wide war would destroy European civilization, which included Germany. Only the Soviet Union and international communism, he argued, would benefit from such a struggle.

Until 1937, Hitler concentrated upon securing power at home. Not until then did he explicitly tell his military commanders that Germany's problems could only be solved by war. This war he forecast for 1943, by which time he predicted Germany's rearmament would be complete. There was strong verbal opposition from the General Staff to such cold-blooded planning, but the interim of six years gave the project an air of unreality. There was time to dissuade Hitler, time for circumstances to intervene.

Events and Hitler's impatience moved faster than General Beck and the others anticipated. In 1936, German troops and armor had entered the Rhineland, until then a demilitarized zone under the terms of the Versailles Treaty. England and France made no protest. Emboldened, Hitler now prepared to move

General Ludwig Beck

against Germany's neighbors to the south and east, Austria and Czechoslovakia.

Austria—small, poor and German-speaking—was ripe for conquest. A local Nazi party, urging union with Germany, introduced political turmoil into the little state, while Hitler bombarded its government with a series of ultimatums designed to end Austrian independence. In the spring of 1938, as Nazis rioted in the heart of Vienna, and German soldiers massed at the border, Hitler's Austrian agents engineered a request for German intervention to maintain order, thus opening the way to occupation and ultimate annexation.

After taking a few months "to digest Austria," as Hitler put it, he was ready to unveil a military plan, referred to as "Case Green," for the occupation of northern Czechoslovakia, called the Sudetenland. Here he used the excuse that its population was primarily German-speaking. General Beck and his associates foresaw disaster. They had supported Hitler, had followed him fearfully into the Rhineland and confidently into Austria, but Czechoslovakia was different. England and France, her old allies, would never permit a German takeover there. The result, they felt, would lead inevitably to another European war in which Germany could only be the loser.

There were further reasons for military misgivings: the Army had grown great under Hitler. Since 1935, it carried its proper name of the *Wehrmacht,* and rearmament had gone forward at a pace that was gratifying to the generals. But if the Army had grown great, so had Nazi power. Hitler was gradually acquiring complete command of the armed forces, breaking top generals and creating field marshals at will. The time had come to act.

The task was not simple. Since 1933, Germany had become a rigid police state. Hitler repressed all possible opposition. When symptoms of insurrection appeared among the Storm Troopers, the Nazis' private army, he ruthlessly executed its leaders. Four years had passed since then, and the only force which remained strong and independent enough to effect his overthrow was the *Wehrmacht.*

During the summer of 1938, therefore, a cadre of resistance centering around General Beck, began to form in the General Staff. It had a precedent for political involvement set long before by a famous Prussian chief of staff, Count von Gneisenau. Gneisenau had not only shaped the strategy which led to the fall of Napoleon; he had staked his career upon an effort to liberalize Germany into a federal state. As Gneisenau had failed in his efforts to reshape his government, so General Beck would fail. Though a fine desk general and a man of unimpeachable honor, he was not a leader of men. When Hitler began to press his Case Green, Beck urged his fellow generals to resign in protest. In the end, he alone resigned. Others, including General Erwin von Witzleben, General Freiherr Kurt von Hammerstein and General Hans Halder, remained optimistic. On the eve of the invasion of Czechoslovakia, they hoped to arrest Hitler at the Berlin Chancellory, which was included in the Third Military District under von Witzleben's command. Once arrested, Hitler would be tried before the People's Court for involving Germany in a European war and, under a plea of insanity, be committed to an institution. Thereafter, the Army would take political control. Neither the naval nor air force commanders were consulted, as they were known to be thorough-going Nazis.

The planned coup d'état never took place. The plotters blamed France and England, particularly Britain's Prime Minister, Neville Chamberlain, for failure to take a strong stand on the question of Czechoslovakia. Indeed, Chamberlain labored under the conviction that any problem could be settled by two decent, sensible men in a direct heart-to-heart talk. Hitler, of course, was neither decent or sensible, nor had he a heart. He regarded Chamberlain as a weak old fool, and at least in this instance he seems to have been right. "I don't feel sure that we ought not to do something," was all Chamberlain had to say before giving his tacit consent to the partition of Czechoslovakia. So Hitler had his conquest without war or bloodshed. Never had his political stock been so high. With the threat of war averted, all motivation behind the generals' plot was undercut. Whether or not they would

LEFT TO RIGHT: *Benito Mussolini, Party Secretary Martin Bormann, Admiral Karl Doenitz, Adolf Hitler, Reich Marshal Hermann Goering; General Alfred Jodl* (EXTREME RIGHT)

have acted otherwise if Hitler had been less successful remains a moot point. Like Beck, they were honorable men, but they were not men of action.

In the months and years to follow, some remained leading lights of the anti-Nazi aristocracy. But never again were these older generals to come so close to reversing the Nazi tide. As events passed beyond their control, they were increasingly reduced to following orders. The Second World War began in earnest with the invasion of Poland in September, 1939. No longer could Chamberlain call for "peace in our time." Britain and France declared war, but they were poorly prepared for the new techniques of the German "Blitzkrieg," or lightning war.

Poland fell, and after a suitable interval for further digestion, the small nations of Europe were gobbled up. Finally, France was brought to her knees, and England was reduced to a small island power, fighting for survival.

Thanks to the military ineptitude of Germany's ambivalent ally, Italy, German armies had to lend support to Italy's flagging armies in North Africa and the Balkans. Then, in 1941, as if his forces were not already overextended, Hitler activated his fatal and lifelong dream, a dream as old as the Teutonic knights. "Drang nach Osten," or "Drive to the East," meant the invasion and conquest of Germany's vast and uneasy ally, Soviet Russia. The attack began at dawn on June 22, 1941. If Germany's fate were not already sealed, it became so now, and many of the generals knew it. Hitler's declaration of war on the United States the following December only confirmed that fact.

Some of the old guard, like Beck, had already resigned. Of those still serving in the army, some had remained true to their early convictions, while others had marched joyfully into Poland. Times had changed. A coup d'état was far harder to initiate than it had been. To act now would be to undermine and destroy a Germany already locked in deadly strife. Whereas the Prussian elite had increasingly lost power, Hitler had progressively surrounded himself with sycophantic military advisors. By 1941, virtually all command was in his hands alone. At the same time, his secret police had grown in power and were capable of immediately intercepting any overt opposition.

Yet the need to act was greater than ever. The Nazi regime had long since declared itself. It had launched a war with total wantonness—destruction for destruction's sake, and it had undertaken unparalleled cruelties against civilians in both Germany and the conquered territories. The purge of political opponents, particularly of intellectuals and communists, was accompanied by the calculated extermination of European Jewry and the virtual enslavement of whole populations.

What was being done by the Nazis in Germany's name was witnessed with horror by countless Germans. Some deemed it a necessary means to a glorious end. Others, knowing better, turned their backs. Many spoke in whispers of resistance but were frozen to inertia by fear of the ruthless police state. Those who did resist did so with varying degrees of commitment and risk. Weiss-Ferdl, a Munich cabaret entertainer in the mid-1930's, made a mild joke: "You know I saw the biggest Mercedes car on the Ludwigstrasse and there wasn't a Nazi in it." Ferdl went to prison for his lack of respect and had the pluck on emerging to quip, "You know I was wrong about the Mercedes car, there was a Nazi in it." Ferdl got away with this, but by 1937 he had joined the Nazi party for self-preservation. The jester ran a minimal risk. The student who spoke out in anger risked his life. Well-remembered are Hans and Sophie Scholl, who printed leaflets against the regime, and who were discovered and executed early in 1943.

Among the clergy, both Catholic and Protestant, there were

Dietrich Bonhoeffer

some martyrs. Father Bernhard Lichtenberg, Dean of the Cathedral of St. Hedwig in Berlin, prayed for the Jews in 1943 and died a prisoner from causes undisclosed while being transported to the camp at Dachau. Dietrich Bonhoeffer, Protestant and theologian, who taught that Hitler was the anti-Christ, survived him by two years, dying before a firing squad in 1945. But all this at best was resistance by word. These men had no actual power. Even those in higher places could but talk. There were the intellectuals of the so-called Kreisau Circle. Led by Helmuth, Count von Moltke, they would discuss plans for a new Germany after the fall of Hitler, but all along they discounted their ability to promote that fall.

Hopeful that the word might serve as a weapon were Hitler's surviving political opponents, particularly the former Lord Mayor of Leipzig, Carl Goerdeler, who tirelessly and recklessly urged insurrection upon anyone who would listen. In the end, he too would be forced to wait impatiently upon those with physical power to act. It was time for the soldiers to take a stand, and there were many high ranking officers besides General Beck who understood the situation morally as well as militarily. They considered themselves led no longer by a responsible head of state, but by the "anti-Christ." Many honestly believed that the soldier's oath and the code of military duty obligated them to serve this leader against the dictates of a humanitarian conscience. Some refused to face the dilemma. Others, such as General Beck, placed conscience above duty to their government, made plans, but could not bring themselves to act. So it remained for the younger men to rally, to set their lives against Hitler's. Paramount among them was a Swabian aristocrat. Though nearly incapacitated by wounds received in battle, he had become convinced that if any shred of German honor were to be saved, Hitler must be destroyed. What follows is his story.

PART ONE

The Hospital

1

BLACK NIGHT. No sound, no motion, only the blood pumping painfully through his body. From the pain, he knew he was not dead, and in his nostrils were the smells of life and death: sweat, blood, gasoline and burned flesh. Gradually, in the stillness, a kind of dawn came within him. It must have been behind his eyes that he saw them, the little desert birds, sand colored, darting on springwire feet, always in motion. There was more substance to the birds' shadows than to their bodies as they moved among the desert flowers—bright red flowers, like a sudden shower of blood.

Within the dream, he began to feel the terrible desert sun upon his head. It searched with probing fingers for a way inside his skull. Turning, he saw it, blue-black and boiling in a white hot sky, and, as he cried out at the sight, the little birds flew up in a whirling swarm. He tried to shield his face, his eyes, from the boring sun and the attack of the birds, but his arms were leaden and he had no hands. In the heart of a dream from which he could not awake, the birds pecked at his eyes with beaks like needles of fire.

"I'm hurt, Lieutenant. I've hurt myself. Where are you?" His cry cut through drugged sleep. The birds and the sun faded. Blackness again, faint voices, and the sound of an engine idling. Then another hurt, insignificant beside the agony which strung his body on hot wires. From this minor hurt spread oblivion. Claus began breathing, great harsh breaths, as the ground rocked under him joltingly and continued to move. The motion and the breathing rolled him down again into a dark confusion that was neither of this world nor the next.

For a brief time he escaped into mindlessness. The visions returned before the pain. White robes drifted under faint high lamps. "How ill this taper burns!" His lips formed silent words memorized long ago. "Who comes here? I think it is the weakness of mine eyes that shapes this monstrous apparition." The white robes moved around him, floated, divided and moved again. "Berthold, Alexander, it's you!" He saw his older brothers as boys again, then recognized the drawing room of his family's quarters in the royal palace at Stuttgart, a fine place for acting out *Julius Caesar*. The others, all half-forgotten school friends in the play, drifted round him, close, familiar faces, smiling slyly, hiding knives. One raised a book and read, "Gentle friends, let's kill him boldly, but not wrathfully. Let's carve him as a dish fit for the Gods." Closer his friends pressed round. He backed off, his hands up before his face. They were no longer acting out a play. They were the desert birds come back to peck at him, no longer with beaks but with daggers. Blades flashed, the falling points drove him down. "Why? Why? Why?" he asked weakly of the white-robed figures clustering above him.

Someone screamed. Man? Woman? At the brink of death, sex departs from the voice. The white figures had vanished, but someone very near was suffering horribly. At first he could not believe the cry was his. An officer must be an example. He couldn't give in. He must have a talk with that man, he told himself, even as his own lips parted, crying shamelessly for his wife. "Nina, help me!"

This time his call was answered by a real voice, a woman's voice. "The poor Colonel hurts very much." In truth, he had never known such pain. He could not get around it. He could scarcely think beyond it. He tried to open his eyes, and it was as though lemon juice had been flushed into the sockets. He tried to rise to his elbows, and a ragged edge of pain turned like a chip of broken glass inside his head. Any motion cut into him.

"Well, he still has good lungs." A man's voice this time, quite impersonal. "I don't think we'll lose him. Not all of him."

"Colonel . . ." The soothing woman's voice again. "Colonel, can you hear me? You're in Carthage. You mustn't despair. We're shipping you home. That's good news, isn't it? No more desert for you . . . and in a minute no more suffering. Not for a while."

He breathed loudly, the air whistling back and forth as though his lungs were a torn bellows. Then he felt a sliver of ice slide into his arm once more. "No! No!" She was feeding him oblivion through the eye of a steel needle, drop by drop.

"You're one of the lucky ones, getting away from this place. Sleep now. Relax and sleep. Give my best to Munich, my brave Colonel." But the wounded man had passed beyond hearing. He was losing consciousness in the heavy drone of engines, and the heat of the morphine passed through him like the rush of warm brandy when he was a boy at Christmas time. Christmas in Stuttgart; the dear dead days of innocence so long ago. Was he thirteen or fourteen? It was hard to say, but he knew it was Christmas by the sparkling of the snowflakes, like diamond dust against the lamp light. Old memories. Why must they force their way back now? He was sharing a cup of *Schnapps* with his friends as they dressed the school tree with birds and beasts, with chocolate rings and all the white and waiting candles. There was always a warming cup at Christmas, always the tree and the feeling that for a short time there must be happiness everywhere. Was it 1917? Even then, Germany had been losing a war, though they hadn't known it yet. They'd seen *The Lost Christmas Star* at the marionette theater, as they always had. They'd even bought roasted chestnuts and caramel sticks from the old market women. Only the fat goose and the homemade jellies were missing. "Gone for the soldiers," someone had said, "for the offensive that will win the war." Then they'd dressed up as mummers. He'd been the Devil with a long fork, chasing the French. Death had been there as well, sheeted and bleached all white with flour, and angels with wobbling wings beneath a golden star.

Claus von Stauffenberg

They lit the Christmas lamps. How golden they burned, with such a steady light. Yet they were remote, all these things once taken for granted and loved: the school, his family, the old royal palace where his father had been Chamberlain to the King, back when there were still kings in Germany.

They lit the top candles first, careful not to let them fall and set all afire. The lights blurred. Why couldn't he focus? He heard the *tum-tum-tum* of a distant drum, a steady pulsing throb of great engines. He couldn't quite tell whether it came from inside him or not, whether it was something heard or something felt. Then, as if through the final delicate adjustment of a microscope, colors deepened, took firm and monstrous shape. The tiny candles became torches, supported no longer by pine branches but by surging figures. The mass of flaming brands took the shape of a twisted cross, borne aloft by marching men. He heard the mighty rhythm of jack boots falling in cadence, saw in the firelight the flash of spades and helmets, the glitter of bronze eagles. Heads to the side, legs jerking stiffly, the brown and black and flaming army flowed by him. They sang with determined, righteous expressions, tears running down their cheeks. The effect was less of music than of a ferocious butchering of silence. Above the general din there rose a single great voice, full of moist vowels and rolling consonants. It roared above the blare of bugles, trumpets and church bells. Loud and vulgar as the red, white and black flags that raged beneath it, the voice intoned iron words: Homeland, Race, Blood, Soil, Mother, Sacrifice. Behind a trench-coated form, searchlights swept back and forth. They encircled the man's head with light. His glance was aimed straight as a rifle at the horizon, his hands crossed on his breast. He shouted into the echoing microphone, and the crowd bayed back in a delirium of mindless response. "You are mine, and I am yours!"

"Let the children come unto me, for they are mine unto death!" he shouted, and schoolgirls, their fingernails painted with the crooked cross, pressed toward him, moths to the flame. "Let the sick come unto me!" and the sick came, the dying, toward a leader who no longer seemed to wear a trench coat but a white robe. And the sick were cured.

Claus surged forward with the crowd, at one with his fantasy, fighting his way toward the platform where the leader stood. He tried to pull himself up so that he might also touch the healing robe, and only then did he see the face. Oily hair fell almost to the eyes, hard and hypnotic as the glazed stare of a goat. Between those eyes the nose jutted out, fleshy, pale, an artificial nose. It was a stone face, demanding blood sacrifice. Still Claus reached for the curing robe, only to see a jack boot brought down on his right hand; brought down and turned left and right as if it were stubbing out a cigar butt. He screamed and fell back, clasping his mutilated hand, his cry sliding down the scale until it ended in an exhausted groan.

The torches diminished. They were candles again, tall, black, and unwinking. They were grouped around a glistening black box. Death was there. Claus could smell its breath. Except for the sound of shifting feet, the place was still. He edged up, curious and repelled, to see the corpse. It was Stefan George, his old master and friend, the Socrates of his learning years. Then this must be 1933. George had died in December of '33, ten years ago. In death the poet looked like a child again, yet incredibly wise and old. He was powdered and scrubbed, with the smooth face of a little girl.

"He doesn't look dead," said Claus.

"He will before long," commented another mourner.

"But he's frowning."

"That's no frown. That's just a sign it's time for the burial."

But he didn't look dead, only withdrawn into a fit of the sulks. Makeup, the undertaker's pastes and powders, obscured the signs of mortality. George had always had a fancy for such things. Thank God, at least his eyes were closed. Claus had dreaded his glance, dreaded the rendition of George's poem, "The Anti-Christ," which he had been appointed to read over his mentor. Yet the book was in his hand, and he began more from memory than from the text before him. The familiar lines described how the dark lord of all evil returned to the earth, how the people cheered and delighted in his coming. As he recited, there seemed to be a gradual change in the corpse's expression, a softening of the lips. "It's only rigor mortis," he told himself even as the lips parted.

The dead mouth opened, and the poet joined him in a duet, his voice gaining in vigor as he sat up slowly, stiffly, from the waist, the way a drawbridge opens. It seemed so natural that, without breaking cadence, Claus recited to the end and then addressed the corpse: "Being dead—I've often wondered what it's like. It must have an odd effect, psychologically speaking."

"Being alive is stranger still these days," replied the poet.

"Germany has turned a contempt for death into contempt for life. It's rather hard to tell the two apart. And you, Claus, trying to touch that man's foot . . . Claus, my dear boy, I wouldn't have thought . . ."

"But this is only a dream. I never did, not really. Not even in the beginning."

"And I've heard, on quite good authority, that you led a Nazi torch parade in Bamberg."

"Not true, I swear it! That was von Manteuffel. Still, one must grant the Nazis this. They've given Germany back her self-respect."

"Given her enemies. Given her Jews to hate," said the poet. "Cured unemployment with concentration camps and the manufacture of daggers."

"No matter what you say, Germany has learned to hold up her head. As far as Hitler goes, we've simply given him a job. The man is sincere."

"Sincere as the old Popes of the Inquisition. A saintly temper never has compassion for its enemies. You listen to him and you begin to doubt the world's antiquity. You'd think we Germans had just crawled out of the Black Forest on all fours. I must say you got what was coming, Claus. Look at that hand of yours, dear boy. Crushed absolutely flat. But there isn't much else you can expect from a pasty-faced little paper hanger who goes around with a jug of lager in one hand and a revolver in the other . . . leaping up on beer hall tables. And that pilot friend of his, that Goering . . . He published a decree that his wife must be addressed as "Your Ladyship." Honestly, Claus, is there no place left for breeding in Germany? Is the land of Goethe, Bach and Beethoven to be run by plumbers, bartenders and streetcar conductors? The old stone gods will rise up laughing from the smouldering ruins and rub the dust of civilization out of their eyes. My God, Claus, it's enough to make us poets die of shame." With this the corpse sank slowly back, whispering, "History is a nightmare. Let me sleep." His face seemed to be laughing. It was a simple contraction of the facial muscles; rigor mortis, nothing more. "Bury me quickly, Claus. I've had enough of the new Germany. The smell's unbearable."

The dead man lay still. Nothing remained but the burying. In silent accord, they carried the coffin from the funeral chapel out into the glowing day. The priest, a spiral of darkness in the gusty sunlight, tossed wisps of benediction after the funeral procession. Below, the church bell fell silent, its last chime hanging on the air, shivering, a faint thread of sound.

The grave was narrow for so great a box. The grave diggers stood humbly aside with their shovels. The priest, his skirt wind bulged, looked like a panoplied knight mounted on his charger. He swung his censer and recited rapidly in Latin like an auctioneer. Then the coffin began its descent. The ropes rattled against the sides of the box as though a last message were being knuckled from within. Part way down, the ropes at the foot became tangled, and the coffin plummeted into the grave head first.

"My God," Claus thought, remembering how vain the poet had been about his fine head of hair, "he'll be all in a heap." Leaning far into the grave, he tried to resettle the coffin lid, which had come completely off. The jolting seemed to have revived the poet. His eyes were open again. Even in the deep shadows of the grave, Claus could see their glitter. Once more words came from the dead lips. "Just one last request, my boy. If you will give a hand to that Hitler person, perhaps you can spare a finger or two for an old friend." With this, the poet seized hold of Claus's left hand as it rested on the lid. With a shriek Claus pulled back, losing two fingers in the process. The lid banged shut.

Claus leapt away, his mutilated hands pressed together in oriental parody. Sun spanked from the spades of the grave diggers as they turned and fled. The entire assembly rushed away, led by the priest who cruised ahead like a ship with billowing sails. Church bells, black tongued and brazen, boomed and bombillated.

"Easy, easy, you damned fool!" someone shouted.

Grave, priest, marching bands and church bells, all were gone as hot blood fired through Claus's arms, down his legs and up to the crown of his head. His entire body was full of hurt. It was dark. He always seemed to awake in the night. Instinctively, he raised bandaged hands to a bandaged face. "Where am I? What's happening?" The dull stench of sepsis overlaid by antisepsis, the reek of unwashed and dying flesh filled his nostrils. "Where is the light? What's happened to me?" he shouted out loud.

"You're back home, Colonel Stauffenberg," came a voice from the dark. "Safe home at the Munich station. We're about to move you to a hospital."

"Water," he said. His lips clung together. He tried to turn his head. "Water. Has anyone a glass of water?"

"Not just yet, Colonel. Just a little pain killer and then off to the hospital."

"Not that. I don't need that," he told the voice, but no one seemed to listen.

"Poor devil's burning with fever. Let's have that needle." Once more the steel stung into his arm. "All right, men. Into the ambulance. And careful. Drop him again, and it's the Russian front for all of you."

Doors latched behind him. He was in an ambulance, back home again, badly wounded. That much he knew. But it was hard trying to remember what had happened. Weakly he asked the drumming darkness for water, and a voice came, unresponsive. "They say he's up for the Iron Cross. Maybe the Knight's Cross."

"Him or his widow. Either way, I don't envy him."

That was the last he heard as unconsciousness seized him and shoved him down a dark and endless slope.

2

HE LAY in an immense roaring cavern. Vague sounds made dreams pour over him, but they were of a different order this time —less grotesque, with the lessening of drugs in his system; more of history remembered.

"October fourth. October fourth, 1938." The date was something remembered and solid, a bulwark against the confusion and pain that lapped about him. "Think of October fourth, remember how it was then. Don't let yourself slip away. Remember, in the summer, you'd been posted to the logistics section, First Light Division. That was at Wuppertal, under Colonel Hoepner."

Military exercises, Hoepner called them, but they crossed over into Czechoslovakia's Sudetenland without a shot being fired. He could see the tanks rolling ahead under sunny skies. All nature had seemed to celebrate their coming. If that was war, it had been so good, so bloodless then, with women throwing garlands of greenery and flowers onto the turrets and before the grinding treads. "How could I have been so innocent?" he thought, remembering how he'd wanted to climb down from the staff car and shake hands. Even then, his fate and Hitler's had seemed linked, a natural tide on the rise.

Remember the old joke? How did it go? "While Chamberlain took a weekend in the country, Hitler took a country in a weekend." You didn't have to like the man, but he got things done. Within six months he had bullied his way into Austria, taken over the country, and then talked the English and the French out of defending Czechoslovakia. "Peace in our time": that was what Chamberlain called it. Poor old umbrella man. He had a quiet dignity which Hitler would never possess, but Hitler knew how to get what he wanted, and all without bloodshed, it seemed; without so much as a wound in the left hand. It was a victory procession all the way, marred only by that old farmer who stood at the roadside spitting toward the rumbling tanks. "We're rust-proof, old man," they'd shouted, laughing at him as they'd laughed at the weekend joke.

"Think," he told himself. "Remember how it was." If Hitler had only been content with Austria and Czechoslovakia, if there had only been an end to conquest . . . But Hitler's appetite was insatiable. Claus's thoughts began to slide. He seemed to see a monstrous Hitler pressing the nations of Europe, like so many sugar cookies, beneath his black brush of a mustache; a modern parody of Saturn devouring his children. "Get hold of yourself, Claus." The drugs were getting the best of him. "Concentrate on the facts. What happened in the Sudetenland besides the parades and the flowers?"

It was the first time he'd really commanded men. He'd often been told that he had an honest, trustworthy face and an appealing voice, just right for an actor or a diplomat; had a ready laugh which seemed to call forth laughter in others. Such qualities helped, of course, but above all, in the Sudetenland he had developed an almost magical belief in his own ability to exercise command. True, there were few hard decisions in that time of adjustment to German rule. The population had to be fed, the farms kept functioning. There was a desperate shortage of horses and vehicles. Claus furnished yeast for the breweries and requisitioned trucks to deliver the beer. He moved troops out into the fields to help with the harvest, and when they tried to take advantage of the peasants' poverty, he published an order forbidding large-scale purchases by his men. When the glass blowers of Hermannshütte ran out of brown coal, he supplied it. Most of his tasks seemed to place him in the satisfying role of Good Samaritan.

October 16 was another date to remember. He was returning from the Sudetenland, and bloodless conquest had given him a taste for war. It had become the lyric of his life: the spectacle, the homage, the manipulation, the artistry of massive deployment. In it all, he saw a new Reich rising, a Reich combining the creativity of Athens with the soldierly virtues of Sparta.

So good, it had seemed so good at the time but it had faded quickly, with the blood riots three weeks later. Or sooner, with Nina's face perhaps, a distorted mirror of his own triumphant smile. "Don't look at me that way, Nina, after all these years. We killed no one, Nina, not a living soul. Nina? I do love you." He had loved her from the first for her natural gaiety and innocence. She was such a graceful woman, wearing her beauty unobtrusively, almost without notice. But Claus had noticed, and had never turned away. They had been married in September of '33, at the Saint Jakobs Church in Bamberg. That night they watched a torchlight procession outside their hotel. The flames flickered on the rattling glass of the window. Finally, they pulled down the shades. He'd seen a river of new energy, Germany united, while she had seen the corded throats, the open mouths, the eyes, many of them streaming tears of sheer delirium. That was the difference between them. Hers was the personal view, and perhaps the world view, too, for her father had been consul general in Shanghai, Warsaw and Kovno. She had lived beyond the boundaries of Germany, and she loved many foreign places as she loved her home. Claus smiled under the bandages, remembering their arguments: he hopeful or at worst resigned, she despairing.

"Remember Weimar?" he said aloud. "The poverty? The disorder? We couldn't go on with that sort of government and survive as a nation."

"I'm more interested in people than nations," he could almost hear her low voice replying. "We could vote the government out in those days."

"May I remind you, dear, Hitler was elected by the German people."

First Lieutenant
Claus von Stauffenberg,
1936

"And just let them try to vote him out again. He's here to stay, Claus, and you know it."

Well, if he didn't know it then, he knew it now. How could he have failed to know when they opened the camp for political undesirables at Dachau, when they burned books that were "foreign" or "decadent"? He had seen such episodes as the birth pangs of a better society, but they were personal hurts to Nina. She'd refused to discuss the Sudeten affair, which had seemed to him a master stroke of diplomacy. Hitler, he felt sure, would not risk war.

"Not risk war! Claus, darling, haven't you read *Mein Kampf?*"

He hadn't. "Well, I have. It's right there in black and white. War with Russia. You have only to look for yourself."

Her voice whispering through his memory was so real that he started. "Nina?" She was his conscience, a conscience which at times seemed too much to bear. He had called her naive, as indeed she was, and yet he knew she held the best of him. When he spoke of patriotism, she spoke of unnatural boundaries between human beings. When he, with some reluctance, purchased a Nazi flag to comply with regulations regarding Nazi Party Day, Nina said if it were to fly from her home it would hang from the toilet window, and so it did. When he lamely enumerated Nazi contributions to public works, she pointed to the yellow park benches upon which Jews were forced to sit, then to the cemetery where the Jewish kindergarten was obliged to play among the tombstones.

"What do you expect me to do?" he would ask her. "I'm just a junior officer. I have my career." And for this she did not have the answer.

The answer came soon enough on a chill autumn evening in 1938. The early dusk had tasted of winter, and the sound had seemed to him at first the breaking of thin ice. Then he turned the corner where a Storm Trooper from the local barracks was scratching "Jewish Sow" on a shop window. He'd gone halfway through the "o" when the pane shattered, cutting his hand. As though the accident were a malevolent attack directed by the shopkeeper, the trooper had dragged a young Jewish girl from the store. Claus had moved to stop the business, but a cordon of grinning brownshirts with their arms linked had held him back while the girl was dragged off to the barracks. By the time Claus had assembled a detail of soldiers, she'd been forced to clean the latrines with her blouse, and then been released. She'd run off sobbing as Claus approached, and suddenly he'd felt very weary, too weary to follow or try to explain. The exuberance of the Sudetenland at last was gone forever. He'd muttered under his breath, "Bastards. Nazi bastards."

He'd still taken it as a local matter until morning, when the newspapers were full of the murder by a Jew of the third secretary at the German Embassy in Paris, and how patriotic Germans throughout the homeland had risen in righteous indignation. Thousands of Jewish properties had been burned or looted, uncounted Jews had been beaten. Many were killed on that *Kristallnacht,* the "Night of Broken Glass." Strange, he had thought at the time, how patriotic Germans always seem to wear brown shirts. Strange, too, how the government managed to profit from its "spontaneous uprisings." For it was no secret that millions of Reichmarks of insurance costs, confiscated Jewish property, not to mention fines levied against the Jews for provoking the disturbances, had fallen into Nazi coffers. As Claus recalled it now, that was the real turning point in his thinking. He'd felt sick with disgust for Hitler and his loutish gang. What an impression they were making on the world!

"We're moving toward war. Mark my words, Claus." That was his uncle, Count Nikolaus von Uxkull. He could hear the older man's voice: "War within the year, unless the *Wehrmacht* takes measures."

"Measures? What measures?" Claus wanted to know. "The Army's nothing but the people in uniform, and the people love Hitler. More than ever, now."

"If nothing's done," said his uncle, "there won't be a Jew left in the Reich. I can tell you on good authority the Fuehrer has relocation in Poland in mind for them."

"Poland? That's impossible."

"He means to conquer Poland, Claus. Surely you sense it."

Claus refused to commit himself. "What do you mean, relocation? Does he mean to make farmers of them, or what?"

"Hardly farmers, Claus. Fertilizer's more like it. He means to exterminate them. Every Jew in Europe, if we give him the chance."

"That's madness."

"Exactly."

"Uncle, you know I'm in no position to act, even if everything you say is true."

What could a junior officer have done then? What could a colonel do now, when his uncle's predictions had come true? In those days, he'd refused to let it torment him, plunging mindlessly into the work at hand or, in rare moments of leisure, going riding to keep the burden of doubt from his mind. He'd always been a first class horseman. He had good hands, long and square and graceful, equally adept at playing the cello or soothing horses. He'd ridden all his life, long before he joined the family regiment, the 17th Cavalry, at Hannover. Dressage was his specialty. He sat a horse with great style, moving as if he and the horse were one flesh. With Nina's father, he'd gone shares in a fine horse, Jagd, chosen from a stud farm when a foal. But when he felt depressed, it was hard riding he needed: the galloping flow of a great body beneath him, the rapid beat of hooves on earth.

Now, as he lay in pain, his memory of Jagd was partly a drugged dream, partly deliberate recall. He concentrated until he could feel the horse's back between his knees, carrying him toward a high hedge. "Easy, boy. That's it. That's it!" But the horse refused, prancing on stiff legs. Claus urged the phantom on again, and they approached the jump slowly, sidling, hind legs bunching like closed fists. "Now! Now!" He felt the upward flow, up and over and down.

It was a leap without ending, for midway the cool wind that blew into his face became the lifting of a bed sheet. "No—no— no. . . Not over my face!" he shouted, suddenly awake. "I'm not dead! I'm not dead!"

"I'm glad to hear it, Colonel Stauffenberg." A new voice from the blackness. "I'm Doctor Lebsche. Professor Sauerbruch arranged for me to treat you. You're in a Munich hospital, wounded rather badly, I'm afraid. Don't worry. We have a lower death rate here than anywhere else. We don't allow our people to die unnecessarily. We can't exclude death entirely, but we put him on good behavior. I think in your case, Colonel, I can safely say the old fellow's been given a rain check. Not that I intend to minimize your problems."

"I can't see. I don't think I can see at all."

"Ah, here's a bit of blood. That should be on the inside. You mustn't roll about just now, Colonel Stauffenberg. Nurse! Nurse, fetch something to help the Colonel off to sleep. We'll be chatting, Stauffenberg. What you need now is rest, not all this rolling about."

The next voice in his dark confusion belonged to a woman.

"If you want to get better, Colonel, you must be more cooperative. You've broken a couple of perfectly good needles. Did you know that?" She prepared his arm with an alcohol rub for the syringe. He tried to pull away, but again the needle went in. "You're acting like a little boy," she told him as the contents of the syringe flooded into his veins. "There now . . . there. Quiet now." Her voice sounded further and further away, like a nightbound train departing through empty plains. He stretched his toes to touch the rail at the foot of the bed. It was something to cling to, something that would keep him from vanishing completely in the dark. "Now he's drowsy," she crooned. "Soon he'll be better. Soon your wife can come and visit. You want to be well for the children."

Claus heard no more. He had already withdrawn into the insistent chronology of his recollections. It was the only residue of control he possessed. He could still force his brain to marshal the past against the urgings of pain and despair. If possible he would find some meaning in his life. He would start 'way back in late summer of 1939, when armor was being massed in the fields of Gross-Born. It was September first. There was a thick ground mist that hot and humid morning as they moved forward; von Rundstedt's Army Group South advancing into Polish Silesia.

With the Sixth Panzers, Claus had raced toward the Vistula. Low overhead, sow-bellied JU 52's, their trimotors vibrating like wasps, had shaken down fresh fruit along the roadsides. He could still taste the apples near the Wielun crossroads where the news had come through on the field telephone that France and

England had declared war on Germany. "My friends," he had said, "if we are to win this war, we must learn to be patient. It will take at least ten years now." Ten apple harvests. Ten years of harvesting men.

This wasn't Austria or the Sudetenland. There'd been the usual preparations, demands that Germany be granted a corridor to Danzig and the sea, demands that Poland cease the mistreatment of its German minority. Hitler had even staged a phony attack by Poles on German soil. This time Claus knew better, but Hitler achieved his war at last. It had been a dazzling conquest on the maps, but it hadn't been war as war should be. Claus remembered with a bitter smile his father's tales of the Prussian Uhlan who had driven his lance into the belly of a Russian during the first cavalry charge. He had not been able to extract the spear from the fallen man, and, glancing down at his foe, broke into bitter tears until the Russian caressed his killing hand, telling him not to take it to heart.

In Poland, it had been tanks against horsemen. The Polish cavalry had emerged through the evening haze and thundered across the wheat fields with their red and white pennants streaming. The whole earth had been vibrant with the great flood of equine life. What a grand show! Hooves cutting neat "U's" in the frosty ground, heads tugging at bits, manes flowing over low-arched necks, and the riders hurling fragile lances into the panzers' armored flanks. It was the last charge of chivalry, so much better trained in the dance and at kissing ladies' hands than at facing armor-plated machine guns. With the sunset already bleeding behind them, they had died there, horse and man, too human to resist the fire, too proud to turn away.

It was said that years after, the men of the Sixth Panzer awoke from their dreams with the sound of horses' screaming in their ears. For Claus, it was the screaming of two women that would henceforth trouble his sleep. They'd been camped near Wielun at the time and under enemy artillery fire at night. A flicker of lights in a nearby farmhouse had led to an investigation and a firing squad for its inhabitants, a mother and daughter.

Claus had entered the picture only in time to stiffen as he heard the volley and the women's last demented cries.

"What's all this?" he'd demanded of the sergeant major in charge.

"Spies, Captain. They were ordered shot as spies, but if you ask me . . ." The women, terrified by the battle, had been found creeping around their house with a flashlight. "They didn't have the wits to direct the enemy fire," was the sergeant major's opinion.

"Then who ordered them shot?" Claus had demanded.

"Lieutenant Herber. He ordered me to get rid of them."

Herber had been a friend until then. Claus sent for him.

The lieutenant had come quietly, walking as though his boots had springs in the toes. He was the model of a fair-haired Aryan warrior who believed in Hitler as a Nordic god. He was well liked and handsome, with a splendidly chiseled face. Its blank perfection reminded Claus of the Charioteer of Delphi.

"You have a good record, Herber," Claus had begun.

"Thank you sir. I pick my targets carefully." His voice had a minimum of energy. He seemed to speak only out of boredom, his lips rounded as though about to substitute whistling for words.

"Perhaps not carefully enough. You ordered two civilians shot."

"As spies, sir."

"But I'm told they had the minds of children."

"Even children can serve their country," said Herber. His eyes were lowered as if in guilty shame. Only later would Claus realize he was incapable of such emotion.

"Why wasn't this referred to me or to the Colonel? How long has it been your job, Lieutenant, to judge? Herber, I think you enjoyed it. Look at me!"

"Of course I enjoyed it, sir. I'm a soldier. I do my duty with pleasure, sir."

"May I remind you, Lieutenant Herber, this is not the SS. There will be an inquiry."

Herber was visibly stung. He clenched his fists as his color rose. "Very well," he said through his teeth. "In other words, sir, you're having me court-martialed."

"Not in other words, Herber. Those are the exact words."

They stared at each other with the hostility of two tom cats on a fence.

"We'll see about that." Herber's words sounded more like a warning than a promise.

"Dismissed, Lieutenant."

Herber made a great demonstration of the final salute, crashing his heels together, hand out stiff and trembling.

Claus had had some doubts afterward. Perhaps he had gone too far. If Herber hadn't been so damned arrogant, if he himself had been longer at war and more accustomed to its brutalities, perhaps then he would have acted otherwise. But in Herber he saw the image of Hitler, the insatiable destroyer. It wasn't his one-time friend, dispatched to a punitive regiment, that stayed with him and woke him at night. It was the remembered cries of those two uncomprehending women who had sought comfort from the thunder of war in the glow of a small electric torch.

Those baffled cries aroused him now, lifting him through warm and vacant blackness into faint light as though from green sea depths into misty moonlight. As wakefulness came, the screams only intensified. "Nurse! Oh God, Nurse!" They came from a neighboring bed. Claus heard the nurse moving fast.

"Major Frank, what is it this time?" came her voice. The important thing to Claus was that he could see, even through his bandages. He could see, and he told them so with unabashed delight. He could see shapes.

Neither paid the slightest attention to him.

"Nurse," said the patient, "I'm not well."

"Of course you're not well, Major."

"I mean . . . Nurse, is the priest around?"

"Father Baltzer is coming in the morning," said the nurse.

"Nurse, that may be too late."

"Come now, Major, what a thing to say. You're not half so

badly off as Colonel Stauffenberg. You don't hear him com-
plaining."

"I think I'm dying. Nurse? You're still there?"

"Preparing a sedative. That's what you need . . . there . . .
that's better."

"I won't wake up, Nurse. I won't wake up."

In a few minutes the patient was quiet. His breath came and
went raspingly.

"What about you, Colonel Stauffenberg? Are you all right?"
The nurse was a darkness against the lesser dark.

"There must be a moon tonight," he said.

"No, Colonel. It's mid-afternoon."

That was a setback, and yet he could see. He could see
something.

"Nurse," he asked obliquely, "if I were a building, would I
have to be condemned?"

"What a question! Besides, I'm not a doctor."

"But you're a woman," he replied. His wounded nakedness
was growing on him like a toadstool. "What about my face?
Is it badly cut up?" He'd never been vain, never conscious of
clothes, but he'd had a good face, with wide-set, dark blue eyes,
broad cheekbones, a strong chin with a slight cleft. It did no
harm to have a good face.

"I don't know, Colonel. You're still all wrapped up in bandages. You don't look bad to me."

"If you were my wife . . . I mean, would my condition revolt
you?"

"You'd look a hero to any decent woman. You're looking
better every day. With a bit more sleep . . ."

"No," he insisted. "Please, no more needles. I'll sleep without
it."

There was a thoughtful silence as he braced himself against
the needle and the humiliation of being helpless.

"Very well," she said. "You can try."

So he was left in the bandaged darkness of an early spring
evening with the sound of drugged and nightmare slumber

around him. An insistant pulse drummed in his forehead. Stitches in his left leg, which he had scarcely noticed before, bit into his flesh like tiny gnawing rats' teeth. As the last vestiges of morphine drained from him, the pain stabbed through. He stifled a surprised and whimpering cry and managed to lie still, feigning sleep when the nurse returned. She looked in long enough to sneeze twice and then went out again. Later she came with a doctor.

"Is he under sedation?" the doctor asked.

"Not now. He's doing splendidly for a man who's lost so much blood."

"I think we can move him to the recovery ward in a few days."

Again he was alone. All the patients in this ward were alone, struggling, for the most part silently, with death.

He tried the old trick of remembering, of removing his mind if not his body from its hurt, but the undrugged pain was dreadful. He clenched his fists inside their bandages and the effort brought him a new awareness. He couldn't feel his right hand. He brought both arms together. Within the gauze on his right arm there was no hand at all. The left hand was there, thank God, but diminished. Something was missing; he wasn't quite sure. Two fingers? How strange that part of him was buried back there in the desert. Part of him was dead; his right hand without flesh, sinews, muscles, picked clean by ants. What could a man do without a right hand? He began to cry silently. At first he thought it was for his lost hand, but later he decided it was because he was giving up the death he had come to expect. It seemed he was going to have to enter life again, with all its crushing burdens.

3

WHEN CLAUS once more awoke from a sleep that had seemed seconds long and unrefreshing, he was aware of a change without at first knowing what it was. The light! The light and the warmth it carried came from the opposite side of his bed. He'd slept through the night without drugs. Judging from the sounds, the sun had just risen. He heard sparrows, the chattering of a squirrel, sounds which meant for him more than squirrels and sparrows, more than springtime. It meant life, for which he had given up all expectation.

The pulse of life brought the renewal of pain, but at least it was pain without drugs. "Go on and hurt," he told his body. By God, if death didn't want him, he'd make something out of life. He would not be one of those vegetables that sat around veterans' hospitals long after the war was forgotten. "Hurt like hell, but I'll win." This time the thoughts he conjured up were clear and coherent. He was back in the Ardennes forest in 1940. It was spring then, too, with a cathedral light shafting down through the haze. He'd been with the logistics section of the Sixth Panzer Division, trying to supply the tanks which moved too fast for the enemy to form defenses.

He'd been doing a good job. They all did a good, unquestioning job in those days. Submerged in details, he'd seemed as far from the war and its inhumanities as a real estate broker behind his desk. There had been no civilians shot out of hand, nor even any battle casualties. There were no yellow stars of David

THE WESTERN FRONT
SPRING OF 1940
(Before the Fall of France)

Extent of Axis Powers
1939 Boundaries
German Moves
(After Spring, 1940)

NORWAY

SWEDEN

FINLAND

Oslo

Stockholm

EST.

North Sea

LATVIA

Baltic Sea

LITH.

DENMARK

Copenhagen

DANZIG

GREAT BRITAIN

NETHERLANDS

Elbe R.

Berlin

Oder R.

Warsaw

London

BELGIUM

Rhine R.

GERMANY

POLAND

Ardennes Forest

LUX.

Prague

Vistula R.

Paris

CZECHOSLOVAKIA

Danube River

FRANCE

SWITZ.

AUSTRIA

Vienna

Budapest

HUNGARY

RUMANIA

Po River

YUGOSLAVIA

Belgrade

ITALY

Adriatic Sea

SPAIN

Rome

ALBANIA

GREECE

Mediterranean Sea

200 MILES

or removal notices, those signs of moral decay so evident back home. He had seen no closed and tormented Jewish ghettos such as were now said to exist in Poland. There was only the day's task and, more quickly than one could imagine, there had been victory in France. Victory had given him a boyish sense of triumph, ludicrous but irresistible. He'd handed out drinks and cigars to his staff.

He had worked tirelessly throughout the short campaign, only seizing a few private moments each day to keep his core, his inner self, clear and distinct. Less often than he felt he should, he used these occasions to write home. Hard as it seemed to face Nina at times, it was harder still to write to her, putting down words that could not be hedged or taken back. Now he found it impossible to explain to her his fleeting elation in victory.

"Dearest Nina," he began. "You need not worry for my safety. The campaign in France has been nothing but a great shopping tour. I'm told on good authority there's so much perfume in Berlin that the entire city smells like a hair stylist's." He wanted to make her laugh deep in her throat, for he loved her laughter. But he knew, of course, she could not laugh at the fall of France; France of the small songbirds, and the good wine; France, the home of her favorite artists.

His own elation had been hard to sustain after he'd seen the newsreels of Hitler accepting the French surrender at Compiègne. "Did you see that man, Nina?" he wrote. "Dancing like a Hottentot? This whole French debacle is frightful. Their army is completely routed. I'm not sure they will ever recover. I suppose I could accept that much if it meant peace and a settlement for Europe, but now everyone is singing *Sailing Against England*. I don't think the English ever realize when they're defeated; that is their blind spot. Ours, dear Nina, is that we never realize when we have won. Yes, I think that is our fatal flaw."

How many times in the three years that had passed since the spring of 1940 had he recalled that last letter from France. How many times since then had he said those words to himself. "Our fatal flaw." Greece invaded, the Balkans, North Africa and finally Russia. While still in France, he had gloomily imagined living out his life as a soldier, growing old in uniform, taking part in one victorious campaign after another until a bullet or the years brought him down. He had foreseen his children recruited into the endless war. Now, three years later, the bullet had come —sooner than he had supposed. But the rest of the picture had changed, with Britain and Russia holding fast and American industry behind them both. Now defeat was inevitable. At best, Germany might sue for a reasonable peace. Rational leaders would make the attempt, but if Hitler lived, all must face flaming *Götterdämmerung,* all that they loved must drown in blood so that maniac might live another year or two.

"While I lie here and do nothing. Damn this face of mine! Damn these hands!" He tried to thrust himself into a sitting position and it was all he could do to keep from crying out. He didn't try it again. The nurse offered him morphine, but he asked for a radio instead; anything to keep his thoughts from running away. It was Sunday. Clemens Krauss was conducting a symphony over the *Deutschlandsender,* transmitting from Berlin. After that, on the *Request Concerts* program, came a soldier on surprise leave from Russia. Claus started to reach for the dial, then remembered his bandaged hand. There was no helping it. He had to lie back and listen while the soldier told his astonished family how well the line was being held in Russia, how proud he was that Vienna, Paris, Athens, were now part of the Third Reich. "To me, they were like Christmas presents," said the soldier's voice.

Someone switched off the radio.

"Thank you," said Claus.

"It's Doctor Lebsche, Colonel. Perhaps we could talk a bit. You look better, Stauffenberg."

"I hope I'm in bad shape. I'd hate to feel this way and be told I'm in good health."

"You know, they say the first dozen wounds take the longest

to heal. Is there something you'd like? Anything that would make you more comfortable?"

"What Goethe called for as he died. More light."

"We doctors are in the darkness, just as you are."

"I know that," admitted Claus.

"But I can safely say your right eye is out of danger." The doctor leaned closer for an inspection. "Yes." He smelled of clean things, of toothpaste, soap and rubbing alcohol. At this close range Claus could see his hands clearly, stuck into skin-tight rubber gloves, so form fitted that the contours of each nail showed.

"You are seeing well with your right eye. Am I correct?"

"But the other one is still bandaged."

"Colonel Stauffenberg, I'm told that when you were found, your face, the left side, was in rags. Your hands were in fright-ful shape. There was blood running from your ears and shrapnel in your left knee. That's enough to kill most men. Well, we've saved your leg, and you'll see and hear."

"But my left eye?"

"Nothing; no hope there. I knew a general once who lost an eye. Got himself a tiger's eye from a taxidermist. Used to slip it into his friends' wine glasses at parties. Seriously, Colonel, a man can get along with one eye; yes, and with one hand. Why, I'm told that Field Marshal Goering, when he discovered the old Kaiser's fine collection of uniforms, rushed to the hospital to have his left arm surgically shortened." The doctor laughed without humor, strictly reflex. "I'm sorry, you must think me callous. We try to regard our patients as broken furniture in a repair shop. If we allowed ourselves to be touched by their suf-fering, we'd never get them onto the operating table in time to save their lives."

"When will I be fit to leave here?" Claus asked.

"Early summer, I should say. You'll need some treatment from time to time. We want to give you a right hand. Rubber and steel may seem alien to human flesh, but you'd be amazed,

Colonel. Such a hand often proves itself more useful than one of flesh and blood. You'll have no trouble lighting your pipe, turning the pages of a book. No problem cutting your nails."

"And in the rain, I rust."

"Not with ordinary care."

"I can drive nails with my fist, I suppose?"

"I wouldn't, but it's a point well taken. I had a patient once who learned to open bottles . . . Of course, you won't be going back into active service."

"No. I feel thoroughly demobilized."

"I shouldn't think you'd miss another Russian winter."

"Tell me, Doctor, how is the war going?"

"Officially? The gospel according to Saint Goebbels? There are bottlenecks. The front is straightened. In the end, peace will come, though perhaps only for the dead."

"Stefan George was lucky. He died when it was still good to live."

"In any event, Colonel, the war will get along without you. Your job now is to rest, so we can clear this bed for another hero. Meanwhile, I have good news. Your wife's in town. She'd like to see you."

"No . . . I mean yes, of course. We must talk."

"It will do you both good."

When the doctor left, he pressed no sedation on his patient and Claus asked for none. The pain in his arms was no longer sharp, but it was still remorseless. For some time he wrestled with the hurt in his body and in his soul. The radio, turned low because it was night, gave no relief. Voices came, hysterically announcing bombers over the homeland. He would have preferred the London station for its unruffled calm, but that was forbidden anyway. Presently the air raid sirens, "Meyer's hunting horn" as they were now called, drifted up from the distant city. Patients began to call out. Rubber wheels hissed on the waxed floors. Nurses crackled past in starched white.

The patient next to Claus began to complain with clockwork regularity. His sounds were shrill and inhuman as bursts from the mouth of a bugle. Claus could barely make him out, for he was engulfed in a blizzard of bandages. Burn, probably. Tubes entered the mummy-like figure from a bottle above, drains exited below into another bottle, which huddled in embarrassment beneath the bed. One bottle kept filling another. They were so similar in size and apparent content that Claus felt apprehensive; they might be inadvertently interchanged. There had to be something wrong with a God who made such a world.

Far off, the raid had begun in earnest. It sounded like someone tumbling down endless stairs. The darkened windows glowed now and then as though the rising moon were catching fire. Nina was out there, as well as the children. "God, however strange and unfathomable you may be, protect her. Protect her." More patients were calling out. Nurses bumped together in the dark. They were administering sedation with all the finesse of soldiers thrusting bayonets. Claus was injected before he could protest, and the real world quickly began to drift and slide. The hospital room in Munich melted away, became a staff headquarters behind the Russian front. The bombs became Russian mortar shells. As the pain in his body grew less, Claus fought to hold on to his personal identity. Slowly and stubbornly he forced the impressions of a year ago into an orderly sequence.

Those had been brain- and bone-numbing months. He had traveled to the front to check out unit battle-worthiness, then back to convalescent camps to assess the prospects for return to duty. By mid-January, 1942, Army Group Center was nearly one hundred thousand men short, and the prospect for reinforcements was not hopeful. This was not Poland in 1939. The drive to the East had become a deadly chess game with the Russians. As one who could see several moves ahead, Claus foresaw disaster. The enemy held the board. They had the big battalions now. It was simple statistics, and he tried to keep it as such in his mind.

As a professional soldier, he had little cause for complaint. The Army had been good to him. In only a few years, he had risen to the rank of major. He plunged into his job and submerged his deeper doubts by offering himself to the divisional command for extra work. He had the reputation of never tiring, of always being ready to give advice and to shoulder burdens too great for others. He made few enemies and many friends, none more important than Baron Henning von Tresckow, Chief of Staff to General Kluge, commander of Army Group Center stationed at Smolensk.

Claus liked him instinctively; liked the serious penetrating eyes, the high bony forehead, the firmly planted Roman nose, the strong mouth and chin.

"Stauffenberg, you always smile when you talk. Why is that?"

"I wasn't aware that I did. Sorry," he had replied.

"No, not at all. I just haven't encountered that many good-natured people of late. You have quite a reputation, Stauffenberg. I'm told you work fourteen hours a day, always fresh, always laughing, half the time with some general like myself weeping on your shoulder. By God, Stauffenberg, I have to say it. You remind me of me!" He laughed, showing pink gums. "Stauffenberg, you're a man I would like to have on my side."

"What other side is there, General?"

"I'm not sure you understand my meaning, Stauffenberg. You would agree, would you not, that there are very few fat Jews left in Europe? It's a weakness of mine, perhaps, that I have always been able to forgive the Jews almost anything because of their sense of humor. The English, too, but the Germans . . . I'll make no bones about it. In the beginning I was enthusiastic about Hitler. Yes, very. I used to be a stockbroker, you know, and I thought he'd be good for business. Well, he was, but Herr Hitler is a humorless man. Has he ever been known to laugh, I wonder? Always the cap down and the Fuehrer gaze. Tell me, Stauffenberg, are you familiar with his decree of last June sixth?"

"Not specifically."

"I'm referring to the Commissar Order, demanding the surrender of all Soviet commissars to the SD for liquidation. The order has been generously construed to include Jews, regardless of their politics, age or sex. Stauffenberg, I have seen the execution squads at work. They derive great satisfaction from killing. I've seen them trembling with delight in every joint as they select their victims, whistling as they mow down thousands."

"Surely you exaggerate, General Tresckow."

"Oh my God, I wish I did. Stauffenberg, I wouldn't talk to you this way if I didn't know your reputation. I know what you did in Poland. I've heard you quoted. You're not a Nazi; far from it."

"I'm not sure I know what I am, General Tresckow. I'm not as happy with the Army as I was."

Major General
Henning von Tresckow

"Because we soldiers are the sword in the hand of an unjust master," said General Tresckow.

"I have thought of that," Claus admitted.

"Frankly, I'm aghast at what's happening. Even more so of what will inevitably come. Something must be done."

"I've said that into a mirror once or twice," said Claus, "but fortunately the mirror keeps its secrets."

"It's bad enough for us to serve a mongrel poster painter, but when that creature shows himself to be clearly mad . . . Major Stauffenberg, surely you can see where all this is heading."

"I'm not arguing with you, General Tresckow."

"The point is, Major, I'm prepared to take the necessary steps before it's too late."

"One man alone?" said Claus. "Surely you don't expect . . ."

"Stauffenberg, I'm assuming I have your complete confidence. Yes? Well then, let me elaborate. A man must have comrades. Alone, he hasn't a chance. Fortunately there are a few honorable men left in this rotting world. Do you know about General Beck? I was on his staff back in '38, when Hitler was planning his Sudeten business. Ludwig Beck and some fellow generals were planning a coup. The idea was to arrest Hitler before he could start a war. Of course there was no war and no coup, but it was a close thing. That surprises you?"

"But General Beck has been retired for four years. They say he's not in very good health." Claus had a vision of a sad and wise old face, its expression one of patient resignation.

"He's still strong," said General Tresckow, "though I'll admit he spends too much time with his rose garden. Then there's Field Marshal von Witzleben. Last year he was prepared to move his troops from France to Berlin and take over."

"He, too, is retired," added Claus.

"Major Stauffenberg, there's been talk of a general field marshals' strike. If we can win Manstein over, the whole of our troops on the Russian front might turn against the regime."

"A big 'if,' General Tresckow. What about General Kluge?"

"Ah, Kluge," said Tresckow. "I have influence there. That

excellent general received a reward from Hitler for loyalty. He's a bit ashamed of it. Also, General Stuelpnagel is with us, unreservedly."

"It may sound tedious," said Claus, "but wasn't Stuelpnagel also dismissed for questioning Hitler?"

"True, but he was reassigned to Paris. Paris might just be the key. That, and Army Intelligence."

"General Tresckow, there is some point to all this, isn't there?"

"There is. The key to our problem is one man, Stauffenberg. One little pastry-eating Napoleon, one womanless Hannibal, one breathing, mortal man, the son of an Austrian customs official and the grandson of a tramp."

"There are those who say he's the victim of bad advice," said Claus.

"You know better, Major."

"You would put him in prison?" asked Claus.

"He is a madman. I would destroy him."

"Friendship at times deafens one," said Claus. "I don't think I heard that."

"I will kill him, Major," said Tresckow.

"And you will be a traitor."

"That isn't a word I like."

"It isn't a likable word," said Claus. "It isn't a likable idea."

"All right then, traitor," said General Tresckow. "But traitor to what? To humanity? To God?"

"You know, General, your success will make Hitler a martyr."

"Stauffenberg, have I your confidence?" Claus nodded. "Then please hear me out. Hitler will be flying here presently. While he is at General Kluge's headquarters, I've made arrangements for a bomb to be smuggled aboard his plane. The bomb is disguised as two brandy bottles. Hitler's return flight will take two or more hours. The bomb will be set for half an hour. A tragic air accident, but no martyr."

"And if you are found out?"

"For Germany, God knows. For me, suicide. I'll try to make

it seem a death in action facing the enemy. That would spare my friends any repercussions."

"General Tresckow, if I had the courage to put the muzzle of a pistol in my mouth, I might have enough courage to go on living. But tell me, should you succeed in this mad business, where do I come in?"

"If it's hard to kill one man, it's that much harder to take over a country at war, particularly with Himmlers and Goerings about. The army will have to be ready. There must be sympathetic preparation, Major Stauffenberg. We can't allow Germany to collapse in civil war or there'll be no chance to negotiate a peace with the Allies. You have the confidence of many men in high places, Stauffenberg. Sound them out."

"Wouldn't you think, General Tresckow, that their listening to me may depend on the success of the new Russian offensive? What do you think? Will we get as far as Stalingrad?"

"Oh, yes, Major. And a good many, those that stay alive, as far as Siberia."

"I'm afraid you're correct, General Tresckow. Good luck. You may be doing the right thing."

"Take care of yourself, Stauffenberg." There were no more words between them. The instant of stronger pressure from Tresckow's fingers as they shook hands said everything.

Their first discussion was over. More than Claus cared to admit at the time, they were kindred spirits, seeing the same devil. Claus had left the interview with his doubts reinforced and returned to his own headquarters at Vinnitsa, there to face the black days of autumn, 1942.

Vinnitsa. A cluster of wooden houses in the midst of emptiness. He could still remember that endless Ukrainian sky stretching away to the wastes of Asia. In November, just before the first snows, the low hills were veiled in the transparent green of next year's grass. Even the third range of crests was green, the fourth a fine smoky blue. The hills stretched on and on, and the ceaseless Asiatic wind sucked at a man's body and soul under the steadily deepening gray of the sky.

RUSSIAN FRONT
NOV.-DEC., 1942

Axis Powers and Occupied Areas
Allied Controlled Areas
1939 Boundaries

Arctic Ocean

N O R W A Y

S W E D E N

F I N L A N D

Oslo

Helsinki

Stockholm

ESTONIA

Leningrad

UNION OF

DENMARK

Copenhagen

Baltic Sea

LATVIA

LITHUANIA

SOVIET SOCIALIST

Moscow

Volga River

Berlin

EAST
PRUSSIA

Smolensk

REPUBLICS

GERMANY

Warsaw

POLAND

Prague

CZECHOSLOVAKIA

Kiev

Dnieper R.

Don R.

Stalingrad

AUSTRIA
Vienna

Budapest

HUNGARY

Vinnitsa

Rostov

Caspian
Sea

RUMANIA

Dniester R.

Belgrade

YUGOSLAVIA

Danube R.

Bucharest

Black Sea

ITALY

BULGARIA

Rome

ALBANIA

Sofia

Istanbul

GREECE

T U R K E Y

IRAN

Athens

SYRIA

IRAQ

200 MILES

Mediterranean Sea

Field Marshal Fritz Erich von Manstein

Claus's task in the Ukraine had been the recruitment of native soldiers into the German army, a vital project after the strain of the mid-summer offensives. Recruits at first were easily found, for the Ukrainians had never fancied themselves citizens of the young Soviet Union. They welcomed the invading Germans as crusaders against communism. Besides, they had never liked the Russians. It seemed a golden opportunity, but Claus's efforts were quickly complicated by *him,* as he tersely referred to

Hitler. Claus was determined to keep his volunteers out of the hands of the SS, whose cruelties were clearly sowing a hatred which Germany's children would reap.

"They aren't polar bears," he had insisted when directives from Berlin indicated the Ukrainians did not need winter uniforms. Claus found them the warm clothing, and Berlin then suggested they be tattooed for identification on the right buttock. He laughed this off. "We can't have our men dropping their pants in this weather. Honestly, they aren't savages." Then he continued more seriously, "We can't bribe them with beads and trinkets. They need to be given pride. They ought to receive the Iron Cross when they do something courageous. They ought to have their own officers." Berlin did not agree, and Claus no longer agreed with Berlin. Something had to be done. He was that much in accord with Tresckow. But the prospect of regicide! There must be a less violent way. To this end, he sounded out Field Marshal Manstein on the possibilities of resisting Hitler. Manstein was pessimistic about the Russian campaign, but steadfast in his oath of loyalty. Following a discussion of Hitler's blunders, Claus questioned him directly. "Field Marshal, under just what circumstances would you act against the Fuehrer?"

"Only if I were so ordered," said Manstein.

"And, if I'm correct, you receive commands only from Hitler himself. There is no intermediate link in the chain of command."

"Exactly, Stauffenberg. I think you understand my dilemma. Besides, you can't seriously expect me to move an army against the state when frankly, on this food, I can't even move my own bowels?"

"I recommend my Ukrainian chef. He does wonders with herbs," Claus replied. And so they drifted into banter, with the Field Marshal concealing his doubts and his commitments behind a gloomy smile.

Then came that day in the first week of December, 1942, on the outskirts of Vinnitsa. The day had begun with an altered promise. On waking, Claus could taste the change, stale and dead, the taste of winter. There was a real storm coming. He could feel the cold. High up the wind was singing, traveling fast over the open land. The second difference was the Gypsies. They appeared about noon. Hunger-driven and desperate, they had come out of hiding, no one knew from where, a nameless swarm of tattered migrants with shaggy hair and black luminous eyes in grim nutcracker faces. There was no play left in the children, and the women were as small as their young. Claus hadn't seen Gypsies since his childhood, when they'd passed over dusty summer roads in their patchwork wagons crying out, "Good medicine, long life!" These Gypsies had no such carts, and few horses. Most of their men were gone as well. Like the Jews, they were marked for extermination.

"We'll have to keep them from the SS," he decided, and gave strict orders to that effect. "And feed them." He personally took a stack of field rations to the children. They watched him in such oppressive silence; it had the impact of tortuous noise. Were they friendly, he wondered, these children who looked centuries old? Their faces had become masks, shrunken down except for the eyes, which were enormous. All their strength was in their will to live. "If I tripped and fell," he wondered, "would they help me up? Would they go through my pockets or devour me along with the field rations?" Hands like sparrows' claws grasped for his offerings. The children closed in around him; he felt the impact of frail bodies, panting, breathless. Fingers roved over him like great spiders.

Later he had a stew pot set up for the entire band. They were frightened, undoubtedly, but they waited with their arms clasped behind them. They did not talk or dispute. When the signal was given, they descended on the cauldron, crowding it from sight with silent purpose. The sight would stay with him, but more than that, the smell: a smell of soil and animals and deep poverty, overlaid, it seemed to him, by the smell of pain and exhaustion and abandoned hope. It was not exactly a bad smell, but rather that of human bodies used to the cracking point.

It would have been better if they had left directly. They couldn't become Stauffenberg's wards. But night came with a cold wind, and they were still there. "There's going to be a storm," he said to his aide. "And then where will they be?"

The sound of a violin distracted him. The volunteers were dancing in his honor, vying with one another for his attention. "Stauffenberg's traveling circus," his fellow officers called it. Well, they might laugh, but the volunteers' corps, now known as the Vlassov Army, numbered close to a million men, with an almost feudal loyalty to the foreign "liberators" and particularly to Stauffenberg. For his understanding, they returned a fanatical devotion, but their adoration was a torment to him. Sitting by the campfire, he wondered miserably if he was a Judas goat leading them to the slaughter or back to a serfdom more vicious than anything they had known before.

The Ukrainians circled around their fire in an intent, maniacal dance, stamping hard, spinning with incredible energy and precision, crouching, then leaping high while a drum beat like a heart and the violin darted fast as a hummingbird; alien music that mocked the conquerors with the vastness of Russia.

The stars were being devoured. Soon it would snow. The dancers leapt high, landing on booted toes. Their faces were concentrated and intent, heels touching, toes touching, round again. Then, in the midst of the turning circle of men, the Gypsies made their contribution. Perhaps for sheer love of dancing, perhaps as a small voice of thanks, a woman came. She might have been fifty or twenty. She carried her lean body straight, in the memory of better days. If she had once had beauty, it was gone with malnutrition and the toil of the endless road. Trouble had twisted her face into a mask of permanent pain, but she could dance with the grace of a ballerina. At first she stood with her head held high, swaying almost imperceptibly, as though in response to some inner rhythm. Then she moved forward with a striding gait, shaking out her hair. She skimmed around the square. Thin and light to begin with, she seemed to weigh nothing as she danced.

Overhead the first thunder rolled like a stampede of cattle down the sky, and with the thunder came the first sibilant hiss of driving snowflakes released from the bulging clouds. Her dance went on untiring, and now she was joined by the Ukrainian soldiers. They leapt over the fire in a parody of pursuit, but the Gypsy woman wove in and out, eluding them until she alone was dancing. Once around the fire she revolved, coming to a stop in front of Claus. The firelight licked about her. Her small dark face, a caricature of ecstasy while she danced, now in exhausted repose had for an instant the horrid flame-lit look of a grinning death's head.

The dancing was over. The fire hissed and sputtered in the falling screen of snow. Claus ordered a crate of field rations, saw that the Gypsies got them, and made sure they were on their way. They looked like a flock of plucked birds, seeming not to walk but to be blown by the wind. He noticed that one of the younger women was pregnant. The unborn baby hung from her wasted loins like a shriveled gourd. "I wonder how far she's carried it on foot, and where she'll take it? Wherever she goes, she'll have company before she goes much further. My God, to send human beings off like this." He was ashamed, but what else could be done? The Gypsies stumbled away, seeming to bear the crucifixion of their future with the stolid resolution of another outcast who had borne a wooden cross two thousand years before. At least, thought Claus, they had food for a week.

With the Gypsies' departure, Claus returned to the inn where he had set up temporary quarters. An apple and a "Winston Churchill" sandwich, smoked sturgeon heaped with caviar, had been put aside for him. He ate only the apple. It must have come from last year's crop, for the skin was loose and wrinkled. There was no sound from the snow-swirled square below. A tank stalled in a rising drift winked red lights: "Help! Help!" The tramp of boots, the cursing of men with shovels, was lost in the cottony waste. Strange how a snowstorm could turn a dreary peasant town into another Bethlehem. What was there about snow? One snow was much like another, and yet it put a bond between people, especially the first real snow before Christmas.

Lying in bed, Claus thought of Christmases at home, but

when he slept, something terrible grinned at him through the darkness so that he awoke with a start. Snow still lashed at the windows. The oceanic green of a lightning flash etched out the humble houses, transfixed them in a flickering glare, then finally extinguished them. There followed no doomsday crack of thunder, but only the high howling of the wind. Strange, he thought, that wind should drown out thunder.

By dawn the storm had stopped. The sky was like the leaden back of a mirror, showing faintly molten gold where the sun tried to burn through. The dreary buildings had been changed into marble temples. Each rooftop wore a snow cap, each doorway and window was eyebrowed in cotton. It was too cold for icicles. In Bavaria there were always icicles. In the cemetery, on the Gothic crosses and shapeless headstones, the snow buried already unreadable monuments. "Lord," said Claus to himself, "what am I doing here? What are any of us doing here? Who gives a damn for this crumpled little town except the poor Russian bastards who've lived and died here? Why don't we all go home?"

For breakfast he ate the Churchill sandwich and, instead of drinking *ersatz* coffee, went outside and scooped up a handful of virgin snow. His footsteps left the first fresh prints as he walked toward where the tank had been. It was gone and so were the cursing men. A lone sentinel moved in the white plume of his own breath, saluting as the Major passed by. Beyond him the cemetery and a field of snow-covered boulders. *Boulders?* thought Claus, remembering only flat emptiness here the day before. He was about to start back when he noticed a gaunt pariah dog digging industriously beside one of the stones. He seemed to have unearthed a withered, blackened stick. The stick turned out, on closer examination, to be a human hand, shiny and cracked as coal. Claus dusted off another stone, and another, as realization grew on him. Now he understood. Those flashes had not been lightning, but flame throwers, shooting out their devouring tongues. One body after another he uncovered, as charred as tree limbs after a forest fire. The bodies of the Gypsies lay in entwined heaps, great knots of humanity—children, women, every age except the age of hope and beauty. A mother's arm was twisted tight around her child's mouth as though to cut off a protest from beyond death.

Claus felt his flesh begin to creep. He knew now how much he feared death. The sight and smell were frightful. He lurched away, breathing through his teeth to keep his nostrils closed. At the side of the road, he lost his breakfast sandwich and the apple from the night before. He went on gagging long after his stomach was empty of all but disgust. "I won't forget this. I will never forget this day," he told himself as he started back. Anger came later, after he had absorbed the first shock. Mid-afternoon found him in a staff car on the way to the local SS *Einsatz* Group Headquarters. There he demanded an interview with Gruppenfuehrer Peiper.

"Yes, Major?" Peiper had eyes like steel tacks pinned into a pale bun of a face. He spoke in the sharp, clipped manner which had long been the SS style.

"I wish to report a mass murder," Claus proceeded. "The SS has no authority at my headquarters, and yet they murdered right under my window."

"Really, Major? Then I suggest next time you draw your curtains."

Claus pushed against Peiper, saying through his teeth, "By God, Peiper, it isn't ending like this!"

As Peiper pulled back, rifle shots deep in the nearby forest filled the quiet afternoon with exclamation points. "Partisans," Peiper said, as one might refer to deer or other game. "Partisans are our affair, Major Stauffenberg. So are aliens who steal government property. Your Gypsies were in possession of German food, army-issue food, and that's a fact that won't change no matter how high or how far you complain."

That was the end of the interview. It was not the end of Claus's efforts for retribution. He made the usual paper protests, the inevitable recourse of reasonable men. The only result was an order from Berlin that he was to be recalled, presented with the Eastern Campaign medal, known popularly as the Frozen Meat Badge, promoted and reassigned to the African war theater to gain combat experience. The desert: another world, another war. He would not have volunteered to go, but he was unasham-edly relieved at the prospect. Ever after, hell for him would be white and peopled by hovering Gypsy faces carried on the wind like an aimless swarm of tormented balloons.

He saw those faces in the shadow play of evening as the hospital settled down to sleep and painful dreams. "I'll remember," he thought, "but I won't dream, not for a while." Dreams could not be controlled, so he fixed his good eye upon the ceiling fan. He counted its revolutions round and round, until he began to see be-hind his eye, behind the bandages, the turning of great iron wheels, the train bearing him back to Germany. It had moved slowly, pushing box cars before it for fear of partisan bombs. One could thank the SS for that. Where one might have received an apple from a Ukrainian farmer the year before, a bullet had now become more likely.

He had disembarked at the Berlin Station. Nina had been there waiting. Claus smiled, remembering, and his face felt tight with scar tissue as it had then felt taut with the cold. "You look beautiful," he'd said, tugging her into his arms. She had leaned against him, whispering, "It's so good. It's so good to have you safe home." Then she'd held him off at arm's length as though to convince herself he was flesh and blood.

Suddenly she seemed a lovely stranger. He'd felt oddly em-barrassed, saying, "Nina, it's cold here. Let's go have a feast."

People were calling it a three-sweater winter, the coldest of the war, and they chose the restaurant for its look of warmth. The windows were steamed over. Smoke belched from an ample chimney.

They sat beside the great fireplace, blackened by past flames, suggesting heat to come. Claus ordered a bottle of Kitzinger Mainleite, 1938. "Good enough for Goering's funeral," observed the waiter. He set down two servings of *Wurstplatte,* ten kinds of tiny sausage.

"You do look well," said Nina, "and wearing the shoulder bars of a Lt. Colonel. Yes?"

"Yes, promoted for not making more trouble for the SS."

"Sorry I don't understand."

"And I'm delighted you don't. Let's talk about you. The family. How are the boys?" he asked her. "Do they miss me?"

"Berthold does, especially. The others are so young. You're more of a photograph than a person to them."

"I know," he said. Tears distorted the lenses of his eyes. He could hardly see; everything winked and glittered. "I've brought them presents. It isn't enough, but . . . And little Valerie? I hope she looks like you." He had seen his daughter only once, very briefly, between France and Russia.

The *Wurstplatte* was served with black bread and the butter was darkly spotted from the fish oil with which it was now mixed. Claus remembered the old line, "I cannot eat as much as I would like to throw up." He wasn't very interested in food, but the wine was good and it helped him overcome his pessimism. As long as he had a wife and children, he had something.

They ate the sausage quietly. Nina put some of hers on Claus's plate. "No," he protested, "I'll blow up like a Strasbourg goose."

"Not you, never. You look fine, except for your hands. They're calloused and cracked. I felt them on my cheeks."

"From the cold," he explained. "I won't be going back where its cold. I'm to be posted to our new African empire. They say it's a clean war out there, just one great amphitheater reserved for warriors. No cities, no civilians, no politics, no SS. A big chessboard." The muscles in her cheek moved and she looked away. "I'll get a splendid tan," he went on, trying to make a holiday of it.

Turning back to him, she said, "That's the way I talk to the children, darling. I make it a game. And when they ask me, will Poppa be killed, I tell them not to be silly and to go to sleep. Then in the morning come the casualty lists. So many mothers all over the world lying to their children. Oh Claus." She clasped his hand until the knuckles whitened. Somehow he had known she was going to say something like that, and still it came as a slippery surprise that had to be caught hold of.

"It's more dangerous here than it is out there. One thousand plane raids! You must stay in the country, Nina. And please try to accept the fact that any soldier runs a risk . . ."

"Please, don't say it."

". . . of being killed in wartime."

"Don't talk that way, Claus."

"Nina, there's nothing gloomy about admitting that some day each of us must die. Life isn't made any better by denying the possibility. Quite the contrary. Only people with an idea of non-existence can fully appreciate sun and light."

Hoping he had made an end of the discussion, Claus paid the bill. Though it was a misty day with the promise of rain or snow, they walked into the park. Nina's footprints left slim gashes in the slush. His boots dug graves.

"I think sometimes life can be worse than nothing," she said, as though the conversation had never been interrupted.

"Let's not go on about it," he said, holding her so close that they walked with difficulty, out of stride. Their surroundings seemed a reflection of their melancholy—the thin black drizzle over the Brandenburg Gate, the soot-encrusted cornices of the Bendlerstrasse, the slush and spin of rubber tires.

"At least Africa is always sunny and hot," he said. "I'll come back brown as an Arab. They say it's a privilege to serve with Rommel. He's an inspiring leader, the best we have."

"And he's losing, too."

Claus couldn't deny that. Even in Russia they'd heard of El Alamein, of how the church bells had rung out all over England. Now the Americans were there as well, closing in from the west.

"Still, it's a gentleman's war, Nina. You can't imagine Russia, what goes on there." He couldn't explain. He could talk about battles and defeats, about the details of army life, but he couldn't, wouldn't tell her what was happening behind the battle lines.

"Stalingrad weighs on everyone," she said as though repeating a formula.

"Yes," he agreed, but he had been thinking of other things; of blackened Gypsies in the snow, of box cars locked from outside; lines and lines of sealed freight cars bound for Germany. Even in winter they carried a foul stench of urine and human excrement which seeped through the floorboards and cracks. Sometimes he blamed the human condition, seeing man as soullessly cruel as the insects. Narrowing the focus, he would condemn his Teutonic race as savage, but that was too much a parody of the Aryan myth. More specifically, the Nazis were a regime of psychopaths, but in the end it came down to a single linch-pin holding all together, one keystone supporting the entire evil structure, and that was Adolf Hitler. Tresckow was right. If only there were an officer in the Fuehrer's headquarters capable of taking his pistol to the brute. . . .

4

MORPHINE WAS A THING of the past; pain, too, except when he was taken down to surgery. His memories had lost all distortion and there remained only the task of sifting out the last few months to see if there was meaning and direction there. Staring at the white ceiling above him, he could see every falling snowflake from that January night of 1943 when he had left Germany by plane. All Germany, according to the radio, was concealed by a heavy blanket of snow, safe from Allied bombers, safe for one night at least. Russia, too, must have lain in the grip of white winter. Thousands of miles of embattled men were immobilized. The partisans in the forest and mountain retreats were held back by the danger from their own tracks. The Sixth Army at Stalingrad, that furthest fling of the tide, was doomed to perish in the snow, as all save Hitler seemed to know. It was good to be flying south to Africa, away from it all. Claus had felt almost on vacation as the clouds over Italy cleared away and the Mediterranean glittered beneath them like a vast sheet of frosted glass. Toward dawn, he could see the pale coast of Africa.

Tunis was clearly a city at war, full of the broken backwash of a losing fight. In the harbor, some ships lay with only their stacks showing. Others were turned over on their sides like elephants bathing. Into their gaping wounds proceeded ant armies of prisoners and soldiers, extracting bales, crates, drums of salvageable oil.

Here Claus conferred with Colonel Wilhelm Burklin, whom

he would be replacing as Senior Staff Officer, operations section of the Tenth Panzer Division. Burklin's adopted desert dog had stepped on a German mine while walking with the Colonel. Nothing remained of the dog but the leash, and the Colonel, his left side sprayed with fragments, some still embedded, walked heavily on a crutch.

Burklin was a believer in the curative properties of salt water, and they motored out to Sidi Bou Said, an old town of white villas and little palm gardens with a shining crescent of sand.

"Even here," Burklin complained, "you get that damned smell. Thousands of years of backed-up sewage. I won't miss that, Stauffenberg. It's the smell of North Africa. That, and burned out tanks."

They joined some other bathers who were shouting and tumbling in the sea. The sun was warm, but the water too cold for anyone but a north German. At least it was something pleasant to write Nina about. As they dried off, Burklin got down to business. Fuel: that was the essence of mobilized war in North Africa. There was talk of another offensive against the Americans, Burklin said. "I don't mind telling you, Stauffenberg, you're in for some long days and longer nights. Frankly, I recommend you get a dog with a nose for anti-personnel mines. And heed the babblings of my old driver, Sergeant Bamm. He's a bit loutish, but he knows Africa and he knows how to drive."

Claus met his driver in the morning. Sergeant Bamm was squat and stocky, clad in dirty yellow shorts and shirt. His skin was brown as scar tissue, and his hair looked chewed rather than combed. He shoved a sun-blistered nose almost into Claus's face, and said, "Bamm, sir. I'm your driver, Colonel. Wolfgang Bamm." He had the muscles and posture of a great ape and Claus was not long in deciding he had the mind of one as well.

Bamm walked beside Claus to the staff car, rolling a bit from side to side. "Bad feet," he explained. The shoes they had furnished him in the Hitler Youth had been too tight, the load on his back too heavy, the hikes too long. Since then, he'd ridden whenever possible. The Mercedes staff car was his pride and joy. Though painted in dull desert colors, it was waxed all over; no dust, no fingerprints. "Good enough for the Fuehrer and his lady."

When Bamm drove, he made Claus think of a circus animal, carefully trained to manipulate a runaway machine. Other traffic, whether it went on treads, tires, two legs or four, was merely part of a conspiracy to keep him from his destination. Mercifully, as they drew away from Tunis, traffic subsided. The countryside opened up on either side. Farms with their thin barley fields and occasional palms disappeared, as did the lavender glimpses of the sea. There had been rain, for the plain was miraculously green and painted with small flowers; dwarf iris, sea lavender, red poppies, and the sun-bleached shells of countless snails. Overhead, the sky was hard as a blue-glazed bowl. Sun and sand had burned away the milkiness of European skies, and left the air clear and sparkling as champagne.

By midday they encountered increasingly rugged and unfriendly terrain and a narrow, boulder-strewn mountain pass. Here their progress was obstructed by a motorcycle and side car. Trailing blue smoke, it moved slowly, jerkily. Bamm depressed the horn and the Mercedes engine roared like a lion as he shifted into second gear. The cyclist kept on doggedly, fearing, perhaps, that to pull over would prove fatal to his laboring machine. Undaunted, Bamm met the challenge. Once, twice and then a third time he bumped against the offending object until it wobbled to the rocky shoulder of the road.

"Bumper's sheet steel. Not a dent." Bamm spoke with pride as he shifted into third.

The occupant of the side car was out and shaking his fist as they passed. "My God, that's a general," Claus exclaimed just before the dust of acceleration enveloped the man.

"Italian general," Bamm replied carelessly. The speedometer was approaching 130 kilometers.

Where the hills gave way again to the sunlit plain, they came upon an obstacle which even Bamm was at a loss to circumnavigate. At first it seemed only an Arab town blessed by an unusually deep watercourse. Claus drew no conclusions from the flock of vultures wheeling and tilting in the sky above. As they proceeded, however, it became obvious that the center of the town had been reduced to rubble. The walled kasbah had been burst open and the sun laid bare its tawdry secrets. A vomitous odor hung in the air, which vibrated with flies.

"What's all this?" Claus asked a military policeman who was directing an Arab cleanup squad with small success.

"The Americans. Pulled out in a hurry. Had an ammunition dump in the mosque over there," the man explained, pointing to a pile of rubble which bore no resemblance to the delicate minarets of Tunis. "No time, so *wham!* They blew it up." Now the townspeople, those who had survived, sat in the rubble staring emptily. A few wept and wailed, their voices blending in a curious rhythm which reminded Claus oddly of a Gregorian chant. The more enterprising fumbled through the destroyed objects, turning them over, gazing through and past them. Vultures strolled about, tame as domestic turkeys.

Claus looked around. No chance of backing up and finding another road—there simply wasn't any. With a nod to his driver, he jumped out of the staff car and began helping the M.P. Presently, motorcyclists arrived and behind them a battalion of Tiger tanks, rumbling nose to tail down the narrow street. Groups of stunned Arabs retreated helplessly into the alleyways. The German motorcycles and the staff car were dragged aside, and the tanks simply kept going.

The lead tank, a great gray beetle, crawled into the debris, its cannon an awkward feeler exploring tentatively ahead. The others followed with more abandon, no longer cautious beetles but iron-shod rhinos, butting through clay and mud brick. When they had passed, a burial detail no longer needed shovels. They could do everything necessary with rakes and brooms.

Claus returned to the staff car on unsteady legs. They had their passage now. It was then, as they bounded forward through pulverized remains, that he heard or imagined a human cry. Among so many cries, it was shocking only because it came from beneath the rubble. "Stop! Stop!" He jerked on the brake himself, sent the car screeching sideways to a halt. "There's someone alive down there," he shouted. Bamm looked at him strangely. Still Claus insisted, and he walked back and forth while the Arabs edged nervously nearer. What horrid surprise had this last foreigner in store for them? "If they'd all shut up, I could hear!" Then, turning in a full circle, he bellowed, "Shut up!" They drew back, silenced. Even the rubble must have been frightened by his outcry. It kept its secrets, and nothing remained but to drive on.

"Madness," Claus muttered to himself as they emerged into open country behind the column of panzers. "All madness."

Still, after Russia Claus found those first weeks in the desert exhilarating, almost a vacation from deeper responsibility. He worked tirelessly and refused at first to think beyond each day's task. He particularly loved the nights, which began with the stirring of a breeze after the sun-parched afternoon. Slowly the streets of the small Arab town, their temporary headquarters, would sink into shadow. As the white minaret of the mosque held the last rosy tint of day, the silence would be broken. A few dogs would find their voices. Smoke would begin to rise. A voice would lift in the atonal evening prayer . . . *ay-ah, ay-ay-ah* . . . as impersonal as an occurrence in the weather. At night the flies vanished, the flies that had been at Claus's ears and eyes and nostrils all day long. The smell died down, too. There was no water for bathing. He could get used to his own smell but not to the smell of others, particularly not to the smell of Sergeant Bamm.

Darkness came quickly in the desert. The sun would simply bury itself in the black hills and then the light was gone. Probably the world would end that way. Here, indeed, it seemed to Claus, was the outer limit of content after a day of trying to dredge up water and gasoline for a panzer division on the move in a desert where both fluids were rationed at best. Just being alone in the darkness became luxury. Without love or pity, without demands of any kind, he could stretch out beneath that great, green camel-driver's moon and all those stars. What sharp eyes the Wise Men must have had to single out just one star, and yet what other theater could have accommodated such a drama. At night the desert became a great cathedral, filled with that boundless congregation to which every creature belonged. Then it seemed to offer the one wisdom in this world, humility.

Only in dreams did Russia return to him, the blowing sand in his ears like the hiss of snow, the blackened bodies beginning to stir, to rise up. Then he would awaken with a gasp of cold air and, staring out into the moon-silvered wastes, would see snow still and those abominations moving in the shadows. Then he would lie awake, watching the stars descend, feeling the breeze sharpen before the dawn. The darkness would still be in his eyes when the sun swept up to dazzle him. No wonder men used to worship it. Roosters in the town would announce its coming in a stillness broken only by their cries and the beating of their wings. Then he'd have to wake Sergeant Bamm. It didn't look right for a colonel to make his own coffee. Making morning coffee was a torment for Bamm. It required decisions over which he muttered tonelessly. Should he make coffee with the shaving water or shave in the coffee?

"How is it this morning, Colonel?"

"I'm not going to tell you what it tastes like." Sergeant Bamm took a sip. "Well, doesn't it?"

"I'm sorry, Colonel. It does, indeed."

"Can't be helped. Only I wonder, Sergeant, if you'd mind moving away from the fire. Like Bavarian cheese, you should never be warmed up."

Even this brief banter was cut out when the offensive began. It was heralded by General Rommel, who rode through divisional headquarters in mid-February. One could not say the man's face was heroic. It would not have been chosen as a model for Siegfried or Barbarossa. Rather it was an honest face, the face of a man accustomed to doing the job assigned. As he stood in his staff car, it was the jobs he had done, the victories he had won where others saw only foregone defeat, which gave Rommel

Field Marshal Erwin Rommel

a splendor and a glory that touched them all, hypnotic as martial music. There, thought Claus, was the horror of it all, that they could do such jobs with no more conscience than the machines they manipulated.

Bamm intruded on his reflections.

"He's a damned terror, that's what General Rommel is."

"A great leader," Claus admitted reluctantly.

"And a damned terror, too. He likes the air full of noise and smoke."

They had plenty of both in the days that followed. By February 17, Claus had set up his field phone at Kasserine village, surrounded by a flat stubbly plain. A good blacktop road led away to the mountainous Kasserine Pass and the developing battle. At first there was little air activity, for rain was falling heavily. From a hundred streaming wadis and ditches, tanks debouched down the valley while infantry rose from the long grass to follow them. It was as if a dam had burst somewhere. All raced ahead. But by the time the clouds which had checked Allied aircraft grew old and tattered, fuel was low. Claus could neither beg, borrow nor steal a litre of gas. What hadn't gone to the bottom of the Mediterranean had been exhausted in this last assault. The following day a "command" word came over his field telephone: Rommel had broken off the action.

Until this time Claus had known only victorious war, and that at a distance; a matter of papers, incessant phone calls, little sleep, and the faint mutter of expensive and killing noise. Now rot was setting in. He found himself allocating, instead of panzers and German crews, reluctant soldiers from Austria and Italy; even ex-political prisoners from the concentration camps, men to whom inglorious duties were assigned and who bled only in defeat.

To Claus in particular fell the disposition of troops for the defense of Gafsa, an oasis town full of palm trees and flowering gardens. The men were Italians, and they sat with their heads drooping between their shoulders, hands slack. At best, they dragged their rifles around—like whipped dogs dragging their tails, Claus thought. One could not call them a division, or a battalion; only a body of men. Their major, arriving stiffly in a staff car, glittered even in the heat of March. He was a vision of pomaded hair, white scarf freshly laundered, and desert goggles turned briefly into light bulbs by the sun. When he removed them, there was a despairing hardness to his eyes. If he commanded still, it was only over fellow captives, as lord of the condemned.

Claus assessed the situation accurately, but he launched first into a prepared speech. It was for the sake of their own country, he told the Italians, that they must take their stand. If North

Africa could be held through the summer, no Allied attack could be launched that year against Italy. The Fuehrer could then concentrate a mighty and final thrust against Russia.

Then he took the Italian commander aside. "I have confidence in you, Major," he said. "I have seldom seen troops better behaved."

The Italian Major fabricated a smile.

"They haven't seen bloodshed yet," he replied sadly.

"May I recommend that you don't give them much comfort or relaxation, Major? After all, you Italians began this campaign. You'll have to finish it. Keep your men dirty, hungry and damned weary. Don't let them think a leave is coming. In a few weeks, they'll be willing to die fighting just to have done with it."

"I would have trouble explaining that to them," said the Italian. "I have trouble understanding it myself. Five years in this desert, Colonel, and I would trade the whole place for the dingiest back-alley flat in Naples. I don't know anymore why I'm here."

There was always an honesty near the front which might see a man court-martialed under other circumstances.

"You're taking a risk talking that way, Major," said Claus. "What if I were to say your only purpose here is to survive? To be taken prisoner by the Americans if you're lucky? That would be a criminal sort of advice. What if I said the Americans feed their prisoners exceptionally well? You, as a good soldier, would be outraged."

"I have a brother in the United States, Colonel. A very rich man. He lives in a place called Manorhaven. Very beautiful, with a great vineyard. He has always asked me to visit him."

"Major," said Claus, "we both understand the situation. I expect you to do your duty." Claus saluted, a salute which the Major stiffly returned. "And my respects to your brother."

Claus was stationed near El Guettar when the Allied attack began. The Germans and Italians had been driven from Gafsa by American troops under General Patton. They had exchanged their soft and lush oasis for a razor-backed and rocky line of

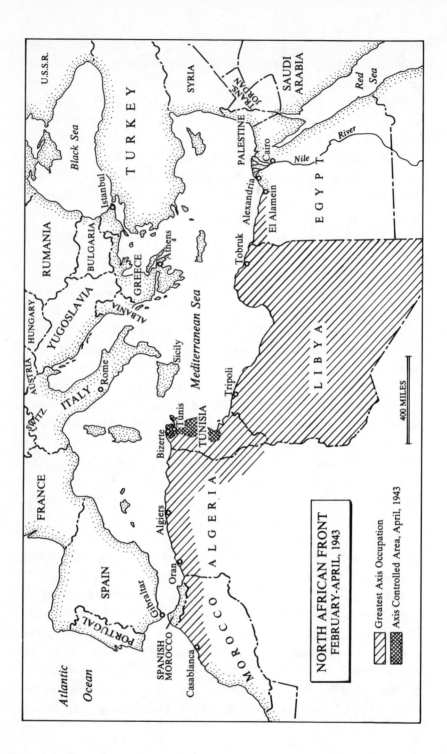

NORTH AFRICAN FRONT
FEBRUARY–APRIL, 1943

Greatest Axis Occupation

Axis Controlled Area, April, 1943

400 MILES

U.S.S.R.

TURKEY

Black Sea

Istanbul

SYRIA

TRANS-JORDAN

SAUDI ARABIA

Red Sea

RUMANIA

BULGARIA

GREECE

Athens

ALBANIA

PALESTINE

Cairo

Nile

River

YUGOSLAVIA

HUNGARY

AUSTRIA

Mediterranean Sea

Alexandria

El Alamein

E G Y P T

SWITZ.

Sicily

Rome

ITALY

Tobruk

Tunis

Bizerte

TUNISIA

Tripoli

L I B Y A

FRANCE

Algiers

Oran

A L G E R I A

SPAIN

Gibraltar

PORTUGAL

SPANISH MOROCCO

Casablanca

M O R O C C O

Atlantic Ocean

hills which sloped to the main road. Here, cactus hedges gave cover from the air. With the dearth of panzers, the defense would depend upon minefields, mortar gun combinations and the Italians out front.

It was a strange feeling to stare toward Gafsa and know it was hostile ground. With good binoculars, Claus might have seen the enemy. There was something wrong about such peaceful observation. When enemies approached, he had assumed they would instantly fling themselves at one another. Toward late afternoon, he could see the little observer tanks out front, seen and lost again in the shimmer of spring heat. Surely it would not be long now. As the enemy drew near, as battle loomed, it was strange, too, how respect for life seemed to grow. He wafted away flies that he otherwise might have squashed.

Midnight came and went; stillness under the stars. Far off, the sky above Tunis flickered, telling of a raid. The clouds glowed from the searchlights. At two in the morning a barrage began, impersonal as jack-hammers in the street. By four, it grew more intense. American long-toms filled the air with express train shrieks. At first their strikes hit high among the brown rocks, then they moved lower down. The ground began to heave like porridge in a hot pan. A near miss sent out a ragged cloud from the white star of the explosion. Eighty-eights winked back their destructive messages in the dark.

Dawn brought a cloudy sky and a gentle breeze and the astonishing realization that rocks and trees still stood. The farms below were still intact, and a few Arabs were out working their fields. The only difference was that the barrage had fallen off to be replaced by the distant mutter of tanks. Here and there pillars of oily smoke rose, tinted blood red by the rising sun. Claus watched the tanks approach like black paper cutouts with the glowing sky behind them. It was a scene of appalling beauty.

Scraps of coded information began coming back from headquarters. Claus's phone rang incessantly as the mechanized cloud rolled in from the horizon. The Italian and German lines waited, silent as forest creatures before a thunderstorm. The first reply came from the giraffe-necked eighty-eights. They could kill a tank at three thousand yards, their solid shot glowing red as it bored through armor. A tank was hit, and rags of black smoke escaped through the hatch before the entire machine went up in flames. Machine guns began firing from cover, their high-pitched fire sounding like the howling of wolves. Claus's ears no longer hurt. His skin felt thick and insensitive, and details began to escape him. He could no longer hear the phone. Then they were pulling back, down the reverse slope, all save the Italians, who had long ago lost heart and were expendable.

At first the withdrawal was by stages, at night whenever possible. Then came the recall to Tunis. At the time, the command post was in an olive grove west of Sidi Mansour, and they were within range of Allied artillery. A near hit had just strewn Claus's maps with mud and glass splinters when the order was given to retreat with all possible haste. Because of Allied planes, they would leave at intervals, spreading the risk. Claus was to go first. Speed and a solitary vehicle in all that waste would minimize the hazard.

Sergeant Bamm was up, lovingly washing the car by starlight for the return journey. He would use most of his daily ration of water so that its radiator would not go thirsty, and in the uncertain light it shone high, long and regal. Claus rolled up his maps to the tune of the engine gulping. Bamm began to jam the throttle back and forth so that it sounded like a car warming up for the *Autobahn* speed trials. By the time they set out, the dawn wind had dropped. A few western stars still challenged the sun.

Retreat was a rattling caterpillar of dusty trucks, transporters with broken tanks, field kitchens, lorries towing wrecked Stukas, dust, gasoline fumes, cordite, and the smell of weary, unwashed men. The retreating tanks were crowded with infantry. Their commanders stood in the turrets, their eyes red lozenges set in talcumed masks, watching the skies for enemy aircraft. Against this irreversible tide came the Italians, plodding on foot. To them had been awarded the hopeless task of delaying the Allied advance. They moved through a sea of dust fine as snuff, a gritty poison in the lungs. The smell of the air suggested that the light of a match might explode the world. Heat mirages added to the poor visibility. On the road, vehicles seemed to rise from oceanic depths through pools of shimmering silver. Bamm was undismayed, steering through the two-way traffic, making Italians leap like so many frogs from his hurtling path.

By nine the heat was oppressive, but Claus preferred it to northern snows. It made him feel alive. The horizon seemed to undulate beneath the rays of the African sun. The shadow of the car and passengers, like a great dancing bat, had more substance than its sunstruck reality. War was left far behind them now except for an occasional reminder: a new grave marked with a helmet, a body left to swell like some hideous gingerbread man.

At noon the wind tasted of the sea, and the fields were full of bluebells, poppies and tulips. Colors, yellow, orange, red, stretched to the horizon. It was spring, but soon the summer sun would shrivel everything in this land beloved only by poets and the migrant few who knew no other. Yet thousands of strangers had already died to possess it. Madness, to fulfill a madman's dream of empire. "I ought to feel guilty or ashamed, being part of it all," Claus thought, but in fact he felt only relief. He'd survived so far. He was enjoying the ride. Perhaps if he had more time to reflect, more sleep for thoughts and emotions to feed upon . . . But as it was, he went about the business of retreat as uninvolved as the image of an actor projected upon a screen.

"Bamm, see if you can get us around this mess. We don't want the others catching us up."

The driver maneuvered ostentatiously through convoy traffic. He was relating one of his anti-Nazi jokes which invariably began, "This one carries five years hard labor," when the first attack came. It was a surprise. A truck out front turned over from a near hit. The occupants sprawled in a heap. No one seemed hurt. In fact, there was an outburst of laughter. The plane, American by its marking, was on its second pass when Claus first glimpsed the fiery disk made by the propeller. Down it came, an unnatural predator with a shrill and penetrating cry. Bamm, his corded muscles bunched together, jerked the wheel around to dodge smoke, dust and scattering men. He could focus on but one thing, and that was saving the car. Off into the fields, back onto the road, off again to avoid the glistening remains of an exploded camel. Claus clung to the seat with the clear realization that he did not want to die.

From here and there in the flowering fields, machine guns chattered back. It was infuriating to contemplate the immunity of that solitary plane as it swung round, tracers curving behind it like a stream of water from a hose. Tiny black streaks of not a hundredth of a second's duration marked the passage of bullets toward the returning target. Then the unbelievable happened. The plane coughed out a great cloud of black smoke and nosed gently over. A flower fell from it, burst open its petals, and the pilot drifted down. Plane and former occupant fell together. First the plane buried its propeller in the earth like a crusader's sword. A minute later the flapping parachute dragged a tiny figure behind it and vanished over a hill.

There was a rush for revenge. Soldiers left their bleeding companions to bound through red poppies and tall white lilies. Only Claus had a car to get there, and he arrived before the others. He saw no sign of the pilot. Soldiers began trotting up, breathing hard and demanding blood, but it took an Arab, bribed with a pack of cigarettes, to point out the pilot's refuge in a dung heap. They dragged him out. He was shaking badly and fumbling for cigarettes. Claus had his pistol drawn. The men waited with rifles leveled. There was sweat on the prisoner's forehead as he looked straight ahead. He knew he was about to be shot, and he would have been had not Claus taken charge in one reflex of sanity, one gesture against the mad pattern of war. At gun point he marched the American off to the staff car. There was grumbling behind their backs, but discipline held as they drove to the road where the convoy was pulling itself together.

"Just my luck," muttered Bamm. "A fighter plane down and nobody with a camera handy to take my picture with my foot on it. Damned planes. They make war impossible."

"Would you say that, Sergeant," said Claus, "if we had as many as they have?"

"Of course not. With planes, we might hang onto this desert."

At this Claus threw back his head and laughed, then Bamm gave a growl of amusement. Finally the American, rather like a child who knows not the joke but wants to be part of the laughter of others, joined in the merriment.

Laughter returned in foolish fits and starts as they drove along, not men in a staff car, it occurred to Claus, but newborn turtles scuttling down the beach toward the safety of the sea; turtles who should have made their run by night. Planes were up and hunting for them, like ravenous feasting gulls. Only the vast numbers of the turtles gave them hope that some would survive.

Bamm complained of a desert sore on his elbow. "Everybody gets the bleeding itch. Nobody knows why. Tinned food, sand, the damned flies. You'd get yourself spotted like a leopard all over, Colonel, if you stayed here long enough."

"At least in Africa you can sing what songs you please," Claus replied. "I happen to be rather partial to Heine. He's a Jew, so of course his works are banned back home."

"Colonel, it would be a pleasure if you would sing one. Might relax our passenger back there. Help pass the time," said Bamm.

Exhilarated by the clear air and the sense of having saved a life, Claus was about to open his mouth and oblige when they were attacked for a second time. Desert wise, an English Spitfire swam down from the sun, its motors shut off, a shark. A truck up ahead was hit and swerved crazily. Men leapt out as though catapulted by a huge spring. They took fantastic postures in the air, spinning and hitting the ground like rag dolls. Some lay flat, others crawled for holes in the solid ground.

"Out! Out! Everybody out!" Claus shouted, but Bamm's reflexes if not his heart and soul were committed to saving the car. With accelerator flat down, they slewed off the paved road, pounding from dune to dune, throwing up showers of dirt and sand until they came to an embedded and shuddering stop.

As Claus staggered out, the Spitfire made its second pass, a wild storm of gray wind. "I'm alive," Claus told himself. "I haven't even been hit." The others were not so lucky. He pulled Bamm out of the wreckage. The windshield had burst into his face, carving it into a glistening red pomegranate. Severed fibers and nerves writhed in that facelessness like things seen in freshly turned soil. The American pilot was also dead, his body tattooed with blue and bloodless punctures. Already the flies were seeking him.

Claus was still dragging his sergeant free of the remains when the Spitfire made its third and last pass, coming so low this time that Claus could see the pilot's goggled face looking over the edge of the cockpit. The ripping wind pulled the man's lip into a grin as the guns began to chatter.

A rawhide whip seemed to scald round Claus's leg. He tried to wriggle to shelter like a scissored worm, but found no cover. There was the thunder of falling towers all about him. Dust and sand forced their way between his teeth and he felt a flaming and exploding inside his head. Then everything dimmed as he plummeted through infinite space. Much later he was aware of flies sizzling, and he wondered whether it would have been better to be a fly, witless, bumbling through life without a thought, without remorse or fear or doubt. He felt the smouldering sun, an open blast furnace above him in a sky streaked red and black. Then the sun became an explosion of pain, blotting out everything.

An hour later a second staff car, accompanied by a wireless truck and two dispatch riders, came upon Stauffenberg's bullet-riddled car. "Medic! Over here, medic! We've found Colonel Stauffenberg. At least I think it's the Colonel. Had half his face shot off. Must be dead, poor bastard. God, what a mess."

5

NINA WAS COMING, and he was afraid of her. The nurse
gave him warning. She smacked his pillows into shape as though
they were misbehaving children. She took him under the arms
as though to prop him up.

"I can do that myself," he insisted sharply.

And then Nina was there, walking quickly down the ward.
She looked pale, but she smiled gallantly; an obvious effort, he
decided, and he tried to smile in return. The attempt began spon-
taneously and then froze. He'd seen that smile in a mirror: one
side of his face didn't respond. He had decided then and there to
give up smiling, at least among his friends.

She stopped at the foot of his bed. "Hello, Claus." She cleared
her throat and when she spoke again her voice was steady.
"You're safe home."

"Most of me."

"You won't go away again, will you?" She was formal as an
interviewer, but her gloved hands gripped at the bed's metal
footrail.

"Not likely. I can scarcely move from this bed."

"They told me you'd been killed. For three days I believed
that. But you look fine." He shook his head in disavowal. "You
do to me," she insisted, her voice rising an octave, beginning to
crack.

"Come, Nina, be honest. I look like hell."

Things had to be said, but a strange shy reticence seemed to hold her at a distance, as though he were fragile and might break on contact.

"But I had that tan, Nina. You should have seen it. Maybe it's still there under the bandages. Come, sit down. Here." He patted the bed with his bandaged hand and she came obediently. "I do look a mess, don't I? I've looked in a mirror; once was enough. Nina, the nurse said . . ." But before he could finish, the barrier broke. The weeks of being brave for the children, the nights of not knowing, were at an end. With an almost savage cry, she embraced him. Her tears had the same quality as her laughter—warm, loving, without reserve. "Nina, Nina," he whispered, "what a time to cry. The other patients will think somebody's died."

"I've been so lonely without you. Would you believe . . . would you believe, Claus, I stroked the sleeves of your old uniforms? I missed you so much. If I'd wanted to kiss a letter or a photograph good night, I'd have married one. But now you're home."

"I'm a cripple, Nina, and not a pretty one."

"You were the handsomest man in the world, Claus. You were so beautiful, I never felt sure you belonged only to me. Now I do, and I want nothing more."

"My hands, Nina." He pulled his right arm out from under the sheet.

"Doctor Lebsche will give you a new hand, darling. He showed me how they work. They're marvelous. They really are." Her insistent voice was wholly sincere.

A nurse with liquid byzantine eyes was tending the heavily bandaged patient in the next bed. She had a container of soup and announced dinner by tapping gently on his plaster skull. There came no response. She lowered her ear to the hole made for his mouth, then spoke in weary apology to Claus and his wife. "I'm afraid the Major won't be with us long. He's gone through so much." But they did not even hear her.

"I suppose," Claus said, half joking, "all that lead and iron in my body will give weight to a new career."

"And I'll make you a distinguished patch. The children have

always fancied pirates. Oh, Claus, I love you. I don't care about your fingers and toes." Nina took a shuddery breath. She was still crying, but quietly now. "If I'd only been here to help from the start, just to be with you. How horrible to be elsewhere! Not even to know you were hurt."

From his one good eye, Claus found himself at last beginning to cry. "Oh, hell," he said. "I shouldn't start this. Now you've got me going, too."

For some time they sat in silence, gently linked together. "Am I hurting you, Claus? Tell me if I am."

"No, no," he reassured her, stroking her fine golden hair with his bandaged left hand.

Meanwhile the nurse went by carrying a red screen which she set up about the neighboring cot. She looked exhausted, as if such duties on a fine spring morning should be abolished. Alone and enigmatic within his arctic snow of bandages, the soldier in the next bed had passed beyond fear or pain.

After her first visit, Nina came every day. She brought spring-time with her, like the caressing breeze that flickered down the corridors, blowing out the curtains, tumbling papers, making nurses laugh. She took over many of the nurses' duties as far as Claus was concerned, even to changing his bandages.

"Do you mind if I stick you with this pin?" she asked.

"No, not at all," he replied, and it was true. He might even have been pleased if she'd pricked him, but she didn't. The bandage on his right arm was pinned fast with very professional tidiness. Thus the days of his recovery slipped by into one long timeless day, punctuated by intermittent sleep, and brief, excruciating episodes in the operating room when the surgeons probed for bits of bone and lead. He was moved to a semi-private room, where he began to use a wheelchair; and all the while spring moved toward summer. He would awake to the twitter of birds, two birds, three; what sweet music. There was hope in him again and love, not only for Nina but for the world.

In the beginning, his trips by wheelchair were short: down the corridor and back. Presently he was going outside where the spring breeze whacked up the green slopes and laughed among the flowers. It was the season of regeneration, of sprouting green, of buzzing bumblebees. Everything was in bloom. "If I were a plant," he told Nina, "I'd grow a new hand." Some said it might be done with electrical stimulation one day, but not in his lifetime. At least he was mastering his wounded leg. They began to take short walks. "I'm stronger than you can imagine," he reassured her. "I only need someone to steady me."

"Just don't stumble."

"Before long," he replied, "I won't even limp." He'd always despised a limp, believing it was often used for effect, to attract sympathy. Some men were proud of such badges, as they were proud of dueling scars, but Claus hated ostentation. Now he was limping, too. He demanded that his body obey. For a few paces he marched, his leg throbbing. Then, keeping his face under control, he sat down on a fallen tree trunk. He was drenched with sweat from the effort.

"Don't try so hard, Claus, not yet," Nina said, sitting down beside him. "Lean on me, Claus. I've never really been a help to you before. It makes me happy, so lean on me for a while."

"What more can an old soldier want? A beautiful woman and gorgeous spring weather."

Later, with summer in its first full plumage, the children came to visit, bringing fruit—pears and cherries.

"Your father will be home soon to stay. For good," their mother told them, smiling in anticipation of his agreement. Her eyes were glad. He could not disappoint her.

"Yes," he said. "We'll have lots of time together." He saw himself surrounded by the children, good books, his favorite phonograph records. "After all, what good's a soldier with no right hand? He can't salute, can't even do a respectable Heil Hitler-kins."

They looked very solemn at his attempted joke.

"Come, all of you. Let's walk."

Claus walked now with a stick. They went to a hillside high over Munich. He could feel the wind from the mountains.

"When my leg's healed, when I can really walk, we'll all of us go up to Felsentor. That's a real walk for you." It had always been his favorite spot high above Lautlingen, the ancient home of the Stauffenbergs, high in the mountains of Swabia. Lautlingen . . . Felsentor . . . they sounded in his brain like holiday bells. "We might even look up the ruins of the old Stauffenberg Castle. How would you like that?" They gave enthusiastic but doubting assent, as though they thought he could never mend that much.

Nina must have sensed it, for she added, "Your father will even play his cello again. Did you know he once played beautifully?"

"I played well, not beautifully," Claus corrected her. "And I doubt I shall ever wound your ears with that sort of noise."

"But the doctors said . . ."

"I know. It isn't that. I once had the notion that I could be the best cello player in the world. When I found out otherwise, I gave it up for good. It's walking I need now. Just look at those mountains!"

He gazed off at the seemingly carefree Bavarian summer. Some of his wounds would not heal, but he felt well enough. There were things he would have to ignore and others he would have to forget. He was not Germany's conscience, after all, and with but one eye he could see but half the evil, shed but half the tears. He told himself all this, and still the thoughts came. With rest and returning health, he could not keep them out. What could he do? He'd paid a fair price. His blood was spilt. Why should he do anything more?

"I'm lucky to be alive," he told himself. "I musn't forget that today or ever."

His only visitor of note had been Lieutenant General Kurt Zeitzler, Chief of the General Staff. He was a great toad of a man who chewed constantly on a cigar stub. He presented Claus with a golden wound badge and a Knight's Cross.

Claus questioned the latter. "What's this for? All I did was get in front of some bullets."

"You pulled men from a burning vehicle," said General Zeitzler, "while under fire."

"Dead men, General."

"Let it be, Stauffenberg. Germany needs her heroes now. And we're expecting to have you back in the traces in no time."

"I've heard only the official radio," said Claus. "Goebbels shouting, 'Do you want total war?' and his Punch and Judy show screeching back, 'Yes, yes, yes!' "

"Stauffenberg, I hesitate to bruise your already battered ears with the realities of the situation. In Tunisia, it's all over."

"A strategic withdrawal, yes, I've heard that."

"Unofficially," said General Zeitzler, "over a quarter of a million men were left behind as prisoners. General Rommel has been sent off to build up the western defenses. His stock has fallen."

"And Russia?" asked Claus. "The radio speaks of Operation Citadel to finish off the last Russian reserves. Kluge and Manstein are in charge, I believe."

"In fact, Colonel Stauffenberg, we are awaiting the first Russian summer offensive."

"General Zeitzler, what's happening on the seas?"

"Well," said Zeitzler, "just let me say that our gray sea-wolves are going down faster than we can build them."

"You're saying, General, that Germany will presently lose the war."

"Lose the war, Stauffenberg? I wish that were possible. We've got it, and there's no getting rid of it. Seriously, my friend, I'm in no position for final judgments. The Fuehrer is confident. And they say where the Fuehrer knows, God has but an inkling, and it's none of our damned business."

"General Zeitzler, do you know him personally? The Fuehrer?"

General Zeitzler nodded. "I was never drawn to fanatics," he said, "but when I met the man face to face, his conviction, his power, were overwhelming."

"Still," said Claus, "he's only a man, a small man with bandy legs."

"When you're with him, Stauffenberg, you see only the eyes. They make death seem irrelevant."

"I've heard he's nearsighted, that he goes around hiding his glasses."

"There is greatness in the man, Stauffenberg. Make no mistake," said General Zeitzler. "Stand before him, and then tell me I'm wrong."

"I'd give my life for the opportunity," said Claus slowly. The general accepted this statement without surprise, but Claus was astonished at his own words, as though he were the ventriloquist's dummy through whom another mind had spoken.

"I tell you, Stauffenberg, the generals stand about the Fuehrer slack-jawed, toes turned in. They're barely able to keep the saliva from running out of their mouths when their Pied Piper speaks."

"Why wasn't he killed in the last war?" said Claus. "He had every chance."

"Destiny, Stauffenberg. Destiny. The Fuehrer dwells in his own twilight world of providence and will power. He imposes his ideas on reality, and when they don't match up, reality must go to the tailor's. He looks at the battle maps with an artist's eye. He straightens the lines on paper according to his sense of aesthetics. He moves the pins on the maps."

"But the pins don't move men, General."

"Dangerous thoughts, Stauffenberg. Very dangerous. Officially, I'm here to welcome you back to your duties at such time as your wounds allow. Off the record, I suggest you take your handsome wife in that one good arm of yours and march out of all this business. Get out, Stauffenberg, now that you have the chance. No one will blame you."

With this observation, General Zeitzler left him. Claus lay on the bed neither smoking nor trying to read nor listening to the radio. He gazed up at the slowly revolving ceiling fan. He felt the empty socket squirm as his good eye moved, following the motion which had no beginning and no ending, an eternal circle. He placed the remaining fingers of his left hand on his chest and was comforted by the movement of his heart at work. He lived. He lived while so many were dead. The only teacher was endurance. He had learned much, but at what a tuition fee. Now they were calling him back into the saddle once more. He could sit no saddle as he had before, and Zeitzler had urged him away from involvement.

Sometimes, remembering desert nights, he thought it would be good to lead the simple life like a hermit in a cave, but he knew at the same time he could not accept simplicity or withdrawal. Deep down, he felt he could make things better, and if this was arrogance, so be it. Since his mutilation, he had thought often of death, but death was the ultimate withdrawal. He had never come to a point where he could completely admit nothing remained for him but to die, except perhaps when he was under anesthesia.

His family was an old and honored one, its heritage traceable to the thirteenth century and Hugo von Stophenberg. All the ancestral portraits were armored, sword-girt, uniformed. One portrait that haunted him was that of August Neithardt von Gneisenau. He could conjure up that face in detail, the deep eyes saying "no" to dishonor, "no" to tyranny, across six generations; Gneisenau, who'd turned back Napoleon; Gneisenau, who put his country's good before slavish loyalty to any man. He was no Prussian robot, but came from the old Swabian nobility with a taste for music and the arts, and above all for humanity. Throughout his life, Claus had cherished Gneisenau as the measure of his own conduct. That man would never have been a tool in Hitler's hands. He would not have been stopped by the loss of an eye or a hand. He would not have been satisfied with the role of disabled veteran, a uniformed jelly, telling tales of old battles.

"No, damn it!" The thoughts produced a shift in his mind as dramatic as the opening of a log-jammed river. Claus turned in bed, looked at his ruined left hand with all the work gone out of it. He'd learned about physical pain. There was far worse,

worse than the body's death. The spirit, too, could die. His own
had suffered more grievous wounds than his body. In Poland,
at least, he had done something for humanity's sake; not much,
but something. In Russia he had learned to turn his back, and
in Africa his staff car had rolled over Arabs dead and dying.
Hell's agents were abroad, and they were sometimes quite per-
sonable. He had almost permitted himself to become one, a
torch bearer in the mad delirium of flames which promised to
engulf the world. He'd been hoodwinked by Hitler at first.
Some still were, while others, knowing they were being used,
salved their consciences by speaking of a soldier's oath, of the
old code of honor. Prussian Honor—it made cripples of them
all. They were like Schnitzler's "Lieutenant Gustl" who could
not live with an insult and could not take redress because the
insult came from a commoner beneath his rank. Suicide was
the coward's way, a poor escape when Prussian honor had tied
resolution into knots, but it was not his way. "I hate what's
going on, but what can I do? What can I do now?" All Germany
was soiled. It must be torn apart limb from limb and washed
clean down to the marrow and white bone. But what could one
man do? One man with one eye and only three fingers? Still,
as inexorably as the fan that turned above him, he knew he
must act somehow. It was in his blood, that sense of integrity
and personal honor, that spirit of freedom as fresh and undeniable as the Swabian torrents in springtime. It had come
down to him through generations of formidable men he could
neither deny nor disown. To see it threatened was not so much
a cause for fear as for wild joy at the call to defend and per-
petuate it. Whatever the price in physical pain, he had no choice
but to move. Now that movement was finding a direction. He
had been spared for a purpose. He was no pointless Lazarus
remarkable only because he could walk and talk. He was alive
for a reason. He felt a new pact with destiny. In one way or
another, it had eluded him until now, but today, in the sunlit
hospital room under the slowly turning fan, it had come to perch

on his shoulder. It was destiny that a wounded corporal had begun the war. Destiny, too, that the generals had failed to act. Perhaps it remained for a dismembered colonel to end it.

It would be hard, of course, to prepare Nina. In fact, he could not tell her everything. It was all very uncertain still but he had already begun by saying, half humorously, "You know, dear, I have a feeling that I shall now have to do something to save the Reich."

"Of course you will." She was obviously not listening. "And you're walking so much better, too."

"I can't look the wives and children of the fallen in the eye," he went on.

"And you won't have to," she assured him.

With the summer of 1943 coming on, Claus put off getting an artificial hand. There would be no time to let the bone splinter grow out. So he postponed the operation, feeling inexplicably vigorous and strong, and inexplicably happy. Confusion and guilt were vanishing like the night and a new dawn was surging in him out of darkness and death. He watched with delight.

He received letters from Tresckow in Russia, where things had gone wrong with the bomb plot. He could judge that from between the lines. Writing clumsily at first with his left hand, he announced his present availability for service. A post would soon be opening for him under General Olbricht in Berlin. The writing began to come more easily. What need for two eyes or ten fingers? They only got in the way of one another. So long as a man had a purpose, so long as he could speak and write, so long as his left hand had the strength to pull the trigger or to jerk the fuse from a grenade. . . . In the long run it was that simple: one trigger or one grenade for one man was the key to it all. One boil to be lanced. One poisonous spider crouching at the central web of all their lives, one anti-Christ, must die.

PART TWO

The Conspirator

6

ON JULY 20, 1944, Claus woke in darkness. There was nothing to be done but lie and wait for the dawn which slowly gathered itself behind the star-struck darkness. The clock chimed four times and its announcement stole away his last drowsiness, replacing it with crawling anxiety and the craving to have done.

A pale opal hue had begun to infuse the sky when he finally arose. The confusions and doubts of the night had almost faded away. He dressed quickly in front of a full-length mirror without ever looking into it. Where three fingers could not do the job, his teeth helped out. Fully dressed, he picked up a small pair of pliers, the jaws set in rubber for a surer grip, and began snipping pencils. Three pencils broke with the sound of a dog grinding bones.

From under his bed he withdrew a package about the size of a hip flask. It contained two pounds of hexite, a putty-like plastic explosive of great power. This bomb was equipped with a ten-minute acid fuse to be activated by snapping its glass case as Claus had already snapped three pencils. It had come originally from England, through channels of the Army intelligence unit, the *Abwehr,* then via General Stieff to Claus's Berlin apartment. It was not capable of fragmentation effect, but the explosive had terrific blast potential. Claus wrapped it carefully in a spare shirt and placed it in his briefcase. On top of this, he placed his prepared report on the Reserve Army. He was ready.

His car arrived precisely at six A.M. Claus squared his shoulders, took a deep breath. "Very well," he said aloud to himself. "The business begins."

Claus opened the door before the driver could knock.

"Fine morning, Colonel," the man greeted him. "May I help you with your case?"

"I'm quite an able soldier," Claus told him. "I don't need to ask help from anyone on this earth except to tie my shoes." The truth was, he did not want to arouse suspicion with such a heavy case. Not that the driver was apt to inform, but if things went wrong, it wouldn't do to widen the circle of implication.

It occurred to Claus that it was the same pattern of help refused and subterfuge which had marked another bright summer morning the year before. Then the sun had a warm but gentler touch. He had been with Nina. She had looked so secretly radiant that for a time his depression was lost in her nearness.

"I'm so happy," she said. "Thank you for being home. From now on you'll stay with me and grow old with me and die with me, everything with me. I feel like a girl, Claus; I do. I want another child. Would that make you happy, too?"

He had answered in the affirmative, and yet how could any decent man be happy in Germany?

"Claus, what's wrong? You're making fists."

He laughed out loud. "How can I? I would love to make fists!"

"Well, don't try. Here, let me have your hand." Her eyes were deep blue and completely unafraid of what she saw. "What is it? Tell me, Claus. I know that you're troubled."

"Sometimes," he had said, "I wake up with a bad taste, as if my whole body is rotten. But it isn't me so much, it's this Germany."

"Can't you just put it out of your mind, darling?"

"Not while I'm alive. Nina . . ."

"Let's not be serious, Claus. It's so beautiful today."

"Nina, let me finish. It's Hitler. He's a dragon, Nina, and someone must slay him."

"Of course someone must. But Saint George had two hands.

Claus, not you!" For the first time she looked really frightened.

"Oh, Nina, of course not me. Even with four hands, I'd still have no way of getting near the man." Those penetrating, always honest eyes, by their inquiry and their pleading for the truth, had forced him to lie. "But I can't remain idle entirely so long as the war goes on. I don't mean murder or even anything dangerous near the front. I'm not fit. But Nina, they want me in Berlin. A desk job. You know, paper work, organization."

"Soon?" she had asked. "Must it be soon?"

"Toward the end of summer," he'd confessed. "We still have time together." Her face and eyes remained cast down.

"I'm sorry, Nina. I've hurt you again."

She shook her head. "I knew. I've known all along. I should love you less and help you more."

She was quite innocent and fortunately very brave. When storms came, she had a way of riding the winds like a bird which soars without batting a wing.

So they had walked back silently, hand in hand, the pain growing in his overtaxed leg, until she asked, "Are you all right?"

That had been a year ago, and it jolted him now as though he had missed an unseen step in the dark when his driver asked the same question. "Are you all right, Colonel? You look pale."

"I'm fine," he replied, glaring at his watch. Before the driver could help, he tore open the car door and lurched inside. The case caught on the knob, threatening to pull him back into the street. "Colonel!" The driver moved toward him as he wrestled the case inside. He had begun to sweat.

The driver looked at him questioningly. "A warm day," he said. "Sir, may I remind you there's a plane waiting at Rangsdorf?" No more was said. They drew away from the curb. His scars felt dead and tight as the breeze blew in through the car window.

Women street workers, their skin translucently sallow, looked nearly as drab as the people he'd seen being rounded up in Russia. They poked through the debris of past raids. He'd been

present in March when the Americans had come for the first
time by daylight, droning through a bright and cloudless sky.
People had stood on rooftops, shading their eyes from the sun
in disbelief. Then the bombs had fallen in lazy wobbling strings
and Claus had watched as the green dome of the cathedral on
Gendarmenmarkt had melted in the blast. The golden man on
its pinnacle had swayed, then dived, a perfect double somersault
into the street. Field Marshal Goering, who'd pledged he'd
change his name to Meyer if a bomb ever fell on sacred German
soil, should have been there, but the man they'd been calling
Meyer for over a year now had slunk off to play with his toy
soldiers and trains.

It had been far worse in other cities: from a stalled train he'd
watched the cremation of Hamburg. For three days and nights
the raiders had come on like mechanized doom, glittering golden
bright in the searchlights, a heavenly host met by upward searching beads of tracer bullets. The city glowed red as the bombs
rained down, fountains of earth, masonry, people, thousands of
lives, billions of marks, the precious past and the hopeful future
all up in smoke and to what end? Certainly not a sane one. One
thousand tons of incendiaries fell on burning Hamburg and from
its heart a great sucking column of smoke rose heavenward. The
few visible stars seemed to have withdrawn to avoid being
scorched.

Claus remembered how the train crawled into a suburban
station where Polish prisoners were hopelessly toiling, clad in
sacks stamped with big purple "P's" for identification, with arm
and head holes cut out so that they might see and rake away shattered glass from the roof of the terminal. There the train took on
refugees from the city, some barefooted, others shod in clouts,
specters with hollow cheeks, eyes like black holes, all smelling
of smoke. Claus stared sleepily at this savage world from one
inflamed eye. He had seen death before. It was the look on the
faces of the survivors that shocked and haunted him. In their
dark eyes still flickered the reflection of that consuming fire
storm, from their mouths came wordless lamentation, a kind of

music no instrument could play, the melody of war and destruction, sung by screaming people in flames.

Among these passengers was a young mother with her child. The woman's face was lovely as a madonna's as she rocked her baby back and forth, uttering wordless sounds, *aieee, aiee,* softly, so as not to attract attention. Here were the simple sounds of primordial suffering, and since then Claus thought he could better understand animals, recognizing in their cries, terror, pain and dumb despair. Finally a Red Cross worker came down the car and administered a shot to the woman. Even asleep she clung to her baby. It took four hands to wrest it away, all that remained of it, for the child was jet black from head to toe, cracked and dead as a lump of coal. The sight stayed with Claus thereafter, as if burned into his optic nerve. Sometimes in sleep he would see the mother and child in reversed colors, their eyes incandescent, pulsing with dark light, sadly accusing. Then he would awake in the night, his heart beating fast, thinking, "We would not crucify Him here, we would burn Him to death, over and over again."

That time it had been Hamburg's turn, but it would happen all over Germany, leaving nothing but ashes if something were not done. Berlin's time was coming, he felt sure. "Thank God, Nina and the children are safe in the country," he reflected as the staff car detoured through a street of ruins. Debris covered the pavement. A crumpled wall bore the motto, "Our walls may break, but never our hearts." This had been overlaid in red paint with the words, "Thanks to our Fuehrer." Some still believed that when a bomb demolished a house, it spared the wall on which hung a portrait of Hitler. Bombs were peculiar things. They could tear out an entire block or have their blast absorbed by the thinnest of fluttering curtains.

For the last six weeks, since the Allied invasion of France, there'd been few raids; the planes were concentrating on the war front. There'd been a chance to sleep in one's own bed, not hunched up in some damp and shuddering shelter.

On the way to Rangsdorf, south of Berlin, they stopped and

picked up Lieutenant Werner von Haeften. Haeften was thirty-five years old, a former businessman who'd been badly wounded in Russia. His brother, Bernd, a naval lieutenant, was with him. Bernd was not party to the plot, and there was little conversation on the way to the airport.

"Did you sleep well, Haeften?" Claus asked.

"I dreamt of the devil," his aide replied, "and how he leads a charmed life."

"I feel today will be different," said Claus. Bernd looked at them curiously. No more was said. They had passed from the city into the undamaged suburbs.

Today had to be different. Claus could afford no doubts. He had to assume that every contingent step would go according to plan. The alternative was death and the ruin of all their hopes. Having cheated death once already, he was keenly aware that he had only one head to lose, but there seemed no better cause in which to risk it. He'd been aware of the hazard since reporting to Home Army headquarters in Berlin seven months ago, in September of '43. His official appointment at that time had been as Chief of Staff to General Olbricht of the General Army Office. He was to report November 1, but he'd arrived early to learn the ropes and to confer with General Tresckow, who was on leave from the Russian front.

"It's good to see you again, Stauffenberg," Tresckow had said at their first meeting. "You look like a veteran now." He'd taken the remains of Claus's one hand in both of his. "And it's good to have you with us. You are with us, are you not?"

"I am, General. Without reservation."

"To the death, Stauffenberg? I know you're a family man."

"If need be, General. To the death."

"Good," said Tresckow. "We have lots to discuss. There are people you must meet."

Claus was to discover that General Tresckow, despite his good nature and his sense of humor, was a megalomaniac. He did not weigh consequences or argue morality. He had long ago concluded that the first step toward German redemption was the destruction of Adolf Hitler. To that end his life was dedicated.

"We came very close last March, Colonel," said Tresckow. "Major Schlabrendorff and I put together a bomb that looked like a bottle of brandy. We took it down to Hitler's plane when the Fuehrer was visiting Kluge's Russian headquarters. Colonel Brandt—you may know him—a fine equestrian—took it aboard, thinking it was a gift for General Stieff. Everything went like clockwork. Hitler on board, all the usual rectangular saluting, the plane down the runway and off into the blue with the bomb set to explode in half an hour. But it didn't. Poor Schlabrendorff had to go after it and get it away from Stieff before he tried to drink the stuff, thinking it really was brandy. Seems that everything had worked except the detonating cap. It was a dud. When your luck gets that bad, Stauffenberg, you begin to question divine providence."

Undaunted, General Tresckow had instigated other attempts on Hitler's life. A bomb was carried into the Berlin Arsenal where Hitler was attending an exhibition of war pictures. Hitler had left before the explosive could be detonated. Defeated by Hitler's tight security and erratic scheduling, General Tresckow had then turned to his commanding officer, Field Marshal von Kluge, an irresolute man who had a conscience but lacked courage. If Hitler could be induced to return to the eastern front, Kluge commanded sufficient military strength to destroy him. "Tomorrow, tomorrow, never an outright yes or no," Tresckow commented. "No matter how much you think you need Kluge's sort, you find out later you were better off without him." Still uncommitted, Field Marshal Kluge had been thrown from his overturned staff car and was hospitalized for three months. Meanwhile, Field Marshal Busch, an avid and unapproachable Nazi, had replaced Kluge in his command.

"Frankly," General Tresckow said to Claus, "prospects on the eastern front are not good. I have more hopes for France. We already have the military governor of Paris, von Stuelpnagel, on our side. He's absolutely firm. And I approached von Rundstedt. He seemed to approve the coup in principle, but he said, 'Rommel is young. The people adore him. Let him do it!' And you know, I believe he's right. You know Rommel."

"Indirectly. The men follow him."

"And he's young and vigorous, but he's rather remote and hard to reach. I've heard that he's against killing Hitler. In any event, Stauffenberg, that doesn't concern us now. Just allow me to fill you in roughly. There are a lot of soldiers and civilians in on this business, and I'll just sketch in the important ones for you. It's up to us military men back here to get things started. General Beck's nominally in charge. Of course he's been a bit out of touch since his retirement."

"Five years ago," Claus interjected.

"Yes, but he's a determined old man with a fine reputation. We need his voice if nothing else. The older Generals respect him."

"Who'll command in the field?" Claus asked.

"Field Marshal Witzleben as Commander in Chief. Colonel General Hoepner over the Reserve Army if Fromm won't cooperate."

"I understood Witzleben had been relieved of command for surgical reasons," said Claus.

"Hemorrhoids," came the reply. "He likes to point out that Frederick the Great had the same affliction. It didn't stop Frederick, I doubt it will stop Witzleben."

"And what about the civilians?" Claus asked. "We'll need them in government if the coup succeeds."

"Afraid so. The ex-Lord Mayor of Leipzig is their first choice for Chancellor once things settle down."

"Carl Goerdeler?"

"The same. Anti-Nazi to the core but a loose-tongued gentleman. Hard to convince, too. I can almost guarantee he'll say 'Colonel Stauffenberg, I suggest you try to be more objective.' "

"I've heard he's rather conservative. Favors monarchy, that sort of thing. What about Julius Leber for Chancellor? He's a good man, efficient, progressive."

"I'm not a politician, Colonel. You'll have your chance to

Carl Goerdeler as Mayor of Leipzig

size them up personally. Theodor and Elisabeth Struenck run a kind of salon, you might say, our secret forum for political and philosophical discussion. You'll meet them all there in time. Meanwhile we have work to do, and you're to be a rather important cog in the machinery. I've scarcely scratched the surface but I think you must appreciate we're an amorphous mass at best. Soldiers here and at the front, civilians racing about, some of them hiding and all afraid of the secret police, informers, tapped telephones, torture. We have to have one to hold all the strings, to keep the web together, someone who knows what's going on everywhere."

"I understood that was up to military counter-intelligence. Admiral Canaris and his bunch at the *Abwehr.*"

"You're right. It was. We counted heavily on the Admiral,

and also on his chief of staff, Colonel Oster. He's the one you're really replacing. Oster was our ears, but since last spring he's been under Gestapo surveillance. We just can't risk it any more. It might mean the collapse of everything."

"Is there no other source of secret information, then?"

"Well, yes, rather surprising, too. SS General Count Helldorf. He commands the civilian police in Berlin."

An SS man, lightning bolts on the collar. "Are you sure he's the sort we need?" Claus asked.

"Yes, certainly. He's one of us. One can always tell, I hope. But it's you we're getting at. Now with the *Abwehr* out of the picture, the nerve center has to shift over here to Army headquarters. You'll be our Oster. Officially, of course, you'll simply be chief of staff to General Olbricht. You can trust him implicitly, but he'll be taken up almost entirely with building the Reserve Army. You'll be the one with freedom of movement, making the contacts, particularly where the assassination is concerned. As you're undoubtedly aware, most of our senior members are reticent when it comes to that."

Claus met his new superior that afternoon. "Welcome to the brotherhood of command," General Olbricht greeted him. Olbricht had a round, good-natured face, a face used to honest laughter. Like Claus, he had kept his optimism, and the two worked well together in their dual roles as conspirators and expediters of troops to the battle fronts.

"And Colonel Stauffenberg," Olbricht cautioned him, "don't ever underrate your official job here. Your predecessor shot himself. That's how you got his job, and he didn't have your added burdens."

"Killed himself? How could he?" Suicide had always been alien to Claus's nature.

"Just wait a while. Wait till you see the faces of those boys and old men going to the front. Wait till you start lying awake at night wondering why the faces look so much alike, the ones you're sending out day after day to die."

Following this conversation with Olbricht, Claus faced a

personal decision. He was scheduled for another operation before being fitted with an artificial hand. But events were beginning to gather speed, and it seemed an indulgence for which he had no time. He postponed surgery indefinitely.

Claus found himself assigned to the supply section. Together with the weapons and administration offices, all were subordinate to the Home Army commander, General Fritz Fromm. Fromm sported an array of medals impressive on any hero's chest, but he was a stumbling block, a mollusk clinging to the wrong rock. Claus's attempt to sound him out only led to the comment, "I haven't got a side in this, Colonel Stauffenberg. I'm like God— I keep aloof." An opportunist, thought Claus, straddling the fence, unwilling to jump until he could identify the winning side, and possibly more of a menace than a convinced Nazi would be. As commander of the Home Army, however, he could not be underrated.

Occasionally they continued the dialogue, Claus earnestly, using every humane persuasion, and General Fromm replying with all the detachment of a visitor from another planet. There was no winning him over while Hitler lived, and more and more Claus devoted his time to a plan for taking over the government.

The plan had a code name, *Valkyrie,* and it would be developed at two levels with two sets of orders. Officially, *Valkyrie* was a scheme to activate units of the Home Army to seize population centers in case of rebellion by the slave laborers in Germany. Behind this careful facade, the plan was to evolve into a complete takeover of the government by the Army.

Claus sketched it out on scratch paper. It seemed beautifully simple and flawless there. "Phase one," he wrote, "plan for mobilizing the Reserve Army. Purpose: to crush any possible mutiny of slave laborers." Notation on a separate sheet. "Of course, the foreign workers pose no real security threat. Hypothesis: to Hitler who rose to power through exciting the mob, such a mass of humanity will seem a real danger."

Fleshed out and put on official paper, this plan for *Valkyrie* was submitted through channels to Hitler. In due course his response was received. "At last, a staff officer with brains."

Claus in turn was spellbound by the ready acceptance of his deceit, and with *Valkyrie* on public record, he went on to prepare the second, secret phase.

"ITEM 1: Disposal of Hitler.

ITEM 2: Preparation of orders to be issued upon Hitler's death under the signature of General Fromm.

PURPOSE: Directing the Reserve Army to undertake the following—occupation, first of the city of Berlin, then of other major cities of Europe.

PRINCIPAL OBJECTIVES: Imprisonment of key Nazi and SS officials, occupation of vital government buildings, railroad stations and other communication centers, especially broadcasting stations."

Then came an underlined note: "Immediate command of the mass media, newspapers, wireless, radio, can not be overly stressed. The conspiracy alone must speak. Orders from Hitler's East Prussian Headquarters must be entirely isolated and contained."

There followed a list of reliable forces during those first hours when the SS would still outnumber the Army in Berlin. ". . . The city police, Count Helldorf's command, Guards Battalion of the Gross Deutschland Division with elite tank unit, cadets from Artillery and Armorer's school, two battalions of low-grade home defense infantry. Then from the wider vicinity, infantry from Doeberitz training school, artillery from school at Jueterbog."

At this point they would know success or failure, but *Valkyrie* projected a third phase, not simply the chaotic breakdown of the German state:

"First, orders to be prepared under the signature of Field Marshal Erwin von Witzleben, proclaiming a state of emergency, dissolving the Nazi Party and putting all affairs of state legally in military hands. Notion: Beck, the first chief of state. Subsequent civilian government: Chancellor, Goerdeler, Leber. These and other posts to be decided."

It all seemed simple on paper. The one obstacle to its success was, of course, Adolf Hitler. There was no way round him and the loyalty that attached to him as long as he breathed.

The final decision regarding Hitler was made at the Army's Bendlerstrasse headquarters in Berlin. General Tresckow had always favored assassination, but the conspirators did not eliminate the other recourses out of hand. Would it be possible, as Goerdeler wished, to reason with such a man as the Fuehrer? Hitler had always believed in his own miraculous image. To reason with him would incur his immediate and consuming hatred: he would kill them for their suggestions as a butcher would finish off a crate of chickens. To arrest Hitler now in his secret lair in East Prussia would require at least a regiment of men, and how could that be assembled and moved into position without his knowledge? How could younger officers, trained in the Hitler Youth and bound by a sacred oath to serve their Fuehrer until death, be trusted?

"There is no other way," Tresckow insisted. "We must use force! Eliminate one life, and the whole pattern of loyalty will shift."

"But how?" Claus demanded. "How can we be sure of success? Not with a pistol, surely. He's surrounded by SS guards every minute, and they say he wears a bullet-proof vest and three pounds of steel in his hat."

In the Fuehrer's ghost-ridden day there was but one occasion when he regularly saw outsiders. That was the military conference, held at noon. This was the one fixed appointment in an irregular life, but it would be suicide to draw a pistol under the eyes of the SS.

"Poison?" suggested General Tresckow. "Artful plots have been baked into many a fruit tart."

"You're joking," said Claus. "You know that Doctor Morell tastes all his food."

"Then study the problem, Stauffenberg. That's what you're here for."

There were many unpromising possibilities for Claus to consider: the composition and effect of poisons from a manual on toxicology; long range and trick firearms, including an SS belt with a four-barrel pistol concealed in the oversized buckle. Finally, there were explosives. "So it's come round to that again, has it?" said Tresckow. Meeting alone, they stared at each other across Tresckow's desk, sharing a secret as yet unknown to the other conspirators. "It's a considerable gamble, Stauffenberg."

"I know, General, but it's possible to plant a bomb and get away in time. I'd want that small chance myself."

"Yet a man must be ready to die—unpleasantly." Tresckow regarded the younger man skeptically around his pipe.

"I think I'd have the courage," said Claus, "if it were the only way to kill the anti-Christ."

"Fortunately, my friend, you have no access to the man, and neither have I. No, with those hands of yours it's impossible. We can't afford to take chances. We need a man who's fit."

"I know, I know," said Claus, who no longer mourned the ruin of his body. He had come to view it as something apart from himself, at worst a hindrance to the accomplishment of his chosen mission. "We must look for a soldier who is willing, and who has the opportunity. It won't be easy to find both in one man."

"I'll do what I can from Russia," said General Tresckow, whose furlough was almost over.

"Leave it to me."

"I'll have to. In safe hands, so to speak." Claus laughed. From Tresckow, this came as no offense. They had no fear of what they might say to one another.

Once Tresckow left for the Russian front it fell to Claus to change the theory of *Valkyrie* into an operational plan. He had little time for it during daylight hours when his ostensible duties called for the development of a logistics section. This task he pursued with his accustomed vigor and efficiency. The door to his office on the Bendlerstrasse was always open. He sat inside dictating, taking phone calls, pacing back and forth, occasionally puffing on a black cigar. The huge casualty rates of the summer made for fierce inter-service rivalry for recruits. The Waffen SS and the Navy were officially favored, though Goering, his air force battered and in eclipse, was being palliated with two armored divisions and some parachute groups. It was in this bureaucratic struggle for men that Stauffenberg moiled all day, trying to plug the cracks in the Reich's waterlogged empire with human bodies. From a strategic point of view, troops should have been pulled back from conquered territories they could no longer hold, but this was not the sort of reality Hitler could accept.

After hours, Claus turned his muscular and untiring mind to a large map of *Valkyrie*. Time was short. The Allies were well into Italy, and it was only a matter of time before they would invade France. There was no time for vacillation. A solid start had to be made, and Claus had the organizational ability to take a dozen details and mold them into one concrete fact, neatly laid out. Unfortunately, there was little order here, and no certainty whatsoever.

Never, even before his injuries, had Claus worked so hard, never with such single-minded dedication. He had just begun to realize that circumstance had placed him at the heart of the conspiracy. Others might share his zeal, possess superior talents, even outrank him, but they were under suspicion, in far-off posts offering no ready access to the crossroads of action. Some were civilians with no force at hand but their willingness to risk their own lives. He had become, almost unknowingly at first, the signal center for all; the one who had to tell the arms and legs of *Valkyrie* when to move. Eventually he was spending many nights in his office on the Bendlerstrasse, napping on a couch when his thoughts began to blur. At other times he worked late at the house he shared with his brother, Berthold, in Wannsee. Seldom did he really sleep. A tic had begun in his left eyelid, a wooden winking which the patch covered and which he ignored. Still, it was a warning. Often there were air raids at night. These, too, he ignored as he would ignore a thunderstorm, but there was one terror-filled occasion when an SS car screeched to a halt outside his window. Men dashed forth. Then, as his heart seemed to withhold its beating, they rushed into the building next door.

Only then did he realize he could still know fear. There might come a time of discovery when he would have to act quickly and take his own life. He had a revolver and he drew it out of its drawer to stare into that black eye of extinction; that period to life. He held the muzzle against his one good eye and imagined the angle of the shot which would crash like fire through his brain. The trigger was difficult for him to manipulate. He wasn't sure he had the will to do it, and yet death must come sooner or later. But suicide? The final abandonment of oneself? No. He'd heard of a man who, fearing what his neighbors might say, decided to disguise his suicide as an accident. He wrote his best friend a letter full of the joy of life, and in the process persuaded himself that life was good. Claus had no doubts. In a sane world, life was very good, but the only hope for such a world was the success of *Valkyrie*.

Valkyrie. The name had a kind of magic in it and the thunder of cavalry. *Valkyrie*. It was always in his mind, which quick and retentive as the darting tongue of a frog, searched every possibility, forgot nothing. No chance must be taken. In addition to the primary orders, there were numerous orders for arrest. There were also proclamations to be read over the radio by General Beck, as the new head of state. Here, again, doubts lingered, for Beck had just undergone surgery. For appendicitis, said the optimists. Terminal stomach cancer, hinted those with a gloomy outlook. Either way, General Beck's role in the conspiracy could not be as active as had originally been hoped, and no one else of comparable public stature was available. Nevertheless, preparations for *Valkyrie* moved forward unabated. The actual orders were typed up in the dead of night by Fraulein von Oven, wearing gloves so as to leave no fingerprints. When she became exhausted, the job was taken over by General Tresckow's wife. A heavy-lidded, calm woman, she was as passionately involved in the conspiracy as her husband.

"Good, good," Claus would say, examining the freshly typed orders. Most were already signed and lacked only a date, stamp and hour. "It's always good to have a Tresckow on the job." Yes, on paper it all looked complete and flawless. Yet when it came time to act, what would happen then? Fortunately there was little time for speculation. With the orders complete and filed in General Olbricht's secret safe, there came the task of sounding out and assessing agents in each military district. Most were sympathetic, but, when the time came, would they risk their lives?

Finally, there was the question of the assassin himself. At first it seemed they had found the ideal man in General Helmuth Stieff, to whom General Tresckow had sent the brandy-bottle bomb by airplane. He had access to the Fuehrer's daily military conferences, but Stieff was not a hero. He finally lost his nerve and said so without shame.

Despair gave way to a new scheme—the demonstration before Hitler of a newly designed winter uniform for the army. It was all a question of finding the right model, a problem seemingly solved by General Tresckow, who wrote from the front, "I have a man you may like. His name is Haeften. He will presently be returning home on convalescent leave and would like to model the new uniform." Time was running short then, as day followed day upon the calendar of conspiracy. The uniform was ready. Claus and Olbricht inspected it, taking note of an inside pocket large enough to contain a bomb. A date for the presentation was selected. As the deadline approached, Claus labored tirelessly at the final preparations, exhausting his colleagues, sending them home for sleep, working on alone.

"Claus, you must get some rest," Baroness Tresckow urged him. "You'll be all muddled when the time comes."

"Don't worry. I'm never really worn out." He was not exhausted by sleeplessness, only provoked by it.

General Helmuth Stieff

"You don't have to show off for me, Claus. There's one good thing about sleep, you know. When you're asleep you can do nothing foolish. Please take care of yourself. A lot of us have come to depend on you."

It was the day before Haeften's expected arrival in Berlin. Little remained to be done except work for work's sake. Taking note of the tic behind his black patch and the golden autumn sun at the window, Claus left the offices at the Bendlerstrasse early that day. He did not go directly to his home, but walked in a nearby park. He stood by a lake and watched the leaves, like the curled yellow hands of Oriental children, floating on the slow green water. The trees were almost stripped to the bone.

"I've missed my favorite season," he said out loud. "I'll be lucky if I get another look at autumn. If the others heard me going on like this, they'd think I've cracked up, but I haven't. I'm just a little tired."

He felt lonely in Berlin. He could not afford to be too close to the innocent, and his family was safer kept at arm's length. He was a danger to know, but he had a need just then for a loyal companion, a dog to walk with, perhaps. He would like that sort of companionship in the park. Then he thought of Hitler and his lonely walks with his shepherd dog. The absurdity of it all made him smile. When it was over, then perhaps he would get a dog, or better still, a horse.

It was dusk when he finally reached his quarters on the Tristanstrasse. The outside needed paint, and the inside plaster. A fine dust of plaster lay on the floor. Glass blown in from the windows crunched icily underfoot. It was cold. The electric heater gave no lasting warmth, and the food consumed there came from tins and was usually burned, for neither Claus nor his brother Berthold were housekeepers by instinct or inclination. In fact, the only abiding comfort on the Tristanstrasse was the knowledge that their families were safe in the south.

"Berthold," Claus said on entering, "you're better than having a dog."

"Am I supposed to be flattered?"

"Brother, the charm's wound up, and high time."

"If not already too late," Berthold added.

"The model arrives here tomorrow," Claus told him, locking his jaws against an inclination to yawn.

"Claus, will you get to bed if I bring you something to drink? What do you want, *Schnapps* or some warm milk?"

"I should not urge thy duty past thy might," Claus quoted from the play they'd done together as boys. "I know young bloods look for a time of rest."

"Go on, Claus. Get to bed. You look ready to fall over."

"Don't be daft, Berthold. I never felt better."

But he went along to his bedroom, a room bare of the unnecessary, without symbols or souvenirs, without photographs of his wife or his children; a room like a tombstone without an inscription. He sat down heavily on the edge of the bed. His body lusted for sleep in every fiber and muscle. His head snapped back with a sharp, neckbreaking jerk. "I'd better get to bed if I'm to stay clear in the head," he told himself, and began to undress with the three tremulous fingers of his left hand. He urged them to get control of themselves. When they'd finished their task, he lurched toward the bed and collapsed, half on the bed, half kneeling on the floor. There he slept until he was awakened by air raid sirens. "I'm glad Berthold didn't see me like this," he thought as he crawled the rest of the way under the covers. There he lay as unmoving as a dead man with the warmth of life still in him.

7

AS THE CAR ROLLED ON through the outlying suburbs, Claus thought of his first meeting with Werner von Haeften. . . . It was on a fog-ridden day of creeping cold that the lieutenant arrived in Claus's office on the Bendlerstrasse. He reminded Claus of a young Napoleon, if Napoleon could have been stretched. There was a certain shyness in his manner which suggested his emotions were imperfectly controlled. He's a romantic, thought Claus, expecting the young officer to stutter.

"I understand you were wounded rather badly," Claus began. Haeften's dossier indicated he had been shot clean through the abdomen.

"Oh, well, yes. It was nothing, nothing really. I'm quite ready for duty," he replied. "Why, compared with your wounds, Colonel . . ." He was getting into trouble.

"Oh yes," said Claus, "I'm well enough. One can leave a hand in North Africa and still get along."

"I'm sorry, sir. I meant only that my wounds were insignificant compared to yours."

"I know what you meant, Haeften." Claus could see admiration in the younger soldier's eyes, and for the first time that he could recall he did not enjoy it. He pushed his chair back and stood up. He walked to the window, feeling suddenly ashamed to ask so much more of this boy than he would ask of himself.

He turned around quickly, wanting to have done with it.

"Lieutenant, we must speak plainly, regardless of how horrible it sounds. You know why you're here."

"Yes, of course." And yet despite the unequivocal reply, Claus thought he noticed a slight evasive wariness in Haeften's eyes. "But not the details, sir."

"There is to be a winter uniform modeled presently before the Fuehrer. That uniform will contain a small but powerful bomb with a very short fuse. Whoever models that uniform must take hold of Hitler as he would a lover. Their bodies must be pressed tightly together when that bomb ignites."

"Then the Fuehrer and I will be killed?"

Claus could think of no fitting reply. He sat down again and looked at Haeften. "Look, I can't tell you to do this. Of course it means your death. It's a hateful deed that we think must be done. But only the dead can tell you if it's worth dying for a good cause, and they aren't talking."

"Will there be others? I mean, will others die as well?"

"The staff meetings are crowded. I would say yes, quite likely."

"May I use my pistol instead, then? I'm a good shot."

"Hitler wears as much armor as a Tiger tank," Claus told him. "No, it's all been thought out. It must be a bomb."

"I see." Now it was Haeften's turn to stare out the window. "I didn't know about the others."

"Well, go on, Lieutenant."

"I have a confession, Colonel Stauffenberg. I'm a religious person, and this . . . well, this is not easy for me."

"Lieutenant, what do you suppose it is for me? A picnic?" He laughed. "No, I realize how deadly serious it is for you, and I'm sorry."

Lieutenant Haeften went on, doggedly. "I had a talk with Pastor Bonhoeffer not long before he was arrested. I asked him what a man should do if he had a chance to kill Hitler. You know how he regards Hitler as the anti-Christ?"

"I do. Go on, Haeften."

"Well, I asked him what Christ would do. I mean if Christ

had a gun or a bomb in Hitler's presence, and this is what the pastor said. He said the more he read about Jesus, the more confused he became. You see, Christ was a genius, which makes him hard for ordinary men to predict. Even Pastor Bonhoeffer couldn't tell me what to do. I've had to make up my own mind. Now I'm ashamed of what I'm about to say, but I must say it. Colonel, I've never been able to accept death, no matter how often I've seen it. I've never killed anyone. In spite of that, I could kill Hitler and die doing it. I'm not a coward, but I couldn't kill innocent people."

"We're none of us that innocent, Haeften. Hitler kills millions to bring about peace, his peace of the dead. And we plan to save Germany by killing. It's a mad world. I doubt if there'll be any real peace or any innocence until murder is erased from the dictionaries and cut out of human hearts."

"You may be right. I don't know; I can't think," Haeften answered slowly, as though the balance of the discussion were evolving inside him. "But I know I couldn't put off a bomb in a roomful of strangers. I couldn't."

Claus respected his honesty. "Well, if that's the way you feel . . ."

"I wish I didn't, Colonel."

Claus tapped the desk. "I've felt the same way," he confessed, reluctantly. "I can't deceive myself, so how can I tell others what to do? Killing doesn't take courage so much as a state of mind, and it's a state of mind which isn't natural to Christian gentlemen."

"I'm sorry I've failed you," Haeften said. His eyes glittered with tears.

"It's nothing. I have to ask too much of people," Claus said, but Haeften's failure meant more time lost, time in which uncounted thousands of the innocent would die. "Lieutenant, I expect you're home for good with that stomach of yours?" Haeften nodded. "I've been looking around for an A.D.C. If you'd like to be in this affair without taking lives personally . . ."

Lieutenant Haeften was pitifully grateful. Tears of relief

*Captain Axel
von dem Bussche*

streamed down his face. "It's a chance for which I'm willing to die," he whispered. "I will die for you, Colonel, if I have to, and gladly."

"All right, Haeften, no more about death just now. See your family, and report back next week. You may discover that there are harder things to do than dying. Now I have a bit of work to sort out."

The work, of course, was to find another assassin. Claus again contacted General Tresckow, and a friend of Tresckow's aide was recommended. He was a captain in the Ninth Infantry Regiment who had served in Poland and Russia. The war had been stern for him, and his fragile face, which otherwise might have seemed ethereal, was sternly marked. In his fierce and fearless eyes Claus saw dead men and the endless Russian snows. Unlike Haeften, Captain Axel von dem Bussche was no convalescent. His step was vigorous and athletic as he walked with Claus to the nearby park where they would hold their discussion. For late November, the day was warm and many people were abroad, catching the last of the sun. The very stillness of the afternoon, the passing strangers, seemed to contest their secret partnership.

Then a siren rose in the distance, so thin and faint it might have been imagined. A nearer repetition could not be ignored. The crowd began to thin. Then came the bark of distant anti-aircraft guns and on the western edge of the sky narrow streaks of water vapor appeared behind the American planes like chalk marks on a blackboard. The two officers ignored them.

"I take it," Claus remarked, "that you're not ashamed to associate with a pack of traitors?"

"We're not traitors to the human race," Bussche replied.

"I presume you're acquainted with the details of the winter uniform and the bomb. I've interviewed others, and we must be absolutely certain there'll be no change of heart when the time comes. Fear is nothing to be ashamed of, but it can paralyze a man, and we can't risk that."

"I've been close to death before," Bussche said, his voice soft and clear and totally, as far as Claus could tell, isolated from emotional involvement.

"Others have had humanitarian scruples," said Claus. "The Lutheran Church has always stood against tyrannicide as a deadly sin. If you're a Catholic, as I am, the way's not so clearly closed. I mean, whether or not it's a deadly sin to kill. Personally, I feel everyone creates his own sins."

"I have no sense of God's hatred touching me," said Bussche. "No, and if I'm about to sell my immortal soul to the devil for a mess of pottage, by God, I'll eat that pottage to the last drop."

"You're Catholic?"

"Was. I retired." At Claus's protest he continued, "Yes, I know. One doesn't retire from God. From the Nazi priesthood, then. These black-robed hypocrites, blessing Hitler and his cronies, blessing their flame throwers and gas chambers . . . I'm afraid, Stauffenberg, one has to look elsewhere, inside oneself for faith these days."

By now the bombs were swimming down, waggling their fins through the air like schools of great gray fish. Buildings swayed under their impact like stage scenery. Talk became impossible. The two men stared at the deafening inferno with weary eyes. Madness, it seemed to Claus, had engulfed the world. Madness in Russia where regiments of men died in the cold; madness on the oceans of the world where men died in flaming tankers or sank soundlessly in punctured submarines; madness in the concentration camps of Poland where humanity died when it could work no more; and all because one man remained alive.

High above, a bomber had fallen out of formation and was drifting lower. Fighters were upon it and bright flashes of exploding shells appeared along the bomber's fusilage before it disintegrated. Nine more men snuffed out, yet *he* remained. The impact of the air attack was drifting toward the east. There was a return of separate sounds; the clatter of shrapnel in the trees, the howl of rescue equipment; even, from somewhere, high laughter, saying, we have survived again.

"This damned destruction," said Bussche, "that's what offends me. Man sinning against himself, defiling works of art, human dignity. I'll admit to you, Colonel Stauffenberg, that at first I admired Hitler. But when I found out what he was doing to the Poles and the Jews, I was nauseated. There were times when I wanted to die in action."

"Death can be a solution," Claus admitted.

"This isn't ego, Colonel, but I must be honest. I feel somehow one of the elect."

"Elect?"

"I feel chosen. I don't mean by you."

"By God, then?"

"No, by destiny and duty, I suppose; my background, the thousand and one things that have put me here today. Call it fate, but I feel it means to use me to fashion the future. If I have to die in the process, well, better a good death than a bad conscience."

"You're very young, Bussche, to be so sure of life and duty. I envy you, and I'm grateful you're here. We have precious little time."

"When?"

"As soon as possible. You'll fly to Hitler's headquarters in Rastenburg tonight. The equipment will go by train."

Claus saw the young captain off. They would not meet again, and Claus felt in parting the heavy burden of sending a brave man to his death. This was the very sort Germany would need after the war. He could not get Captain Bussche out of his mind, but pictured him waiting out those last sunny days among the forests and lakes of East Prussia; late autumn days brilliantly illuminated, days which soldiers learn to prize in the hour before attack.

It wasn't to be. The following day the news arrived with Haeften that the train bearing the uniform had been completely destroyed in an air raid on the Berlin railroad yard. There was no spare, and the leather parts would take time to replace. The demonstration was put off. Axel von dem Bussche returned to the front. He would come back in late December for another try, but on Christmas Eve Hitler decided to visit Obersalzberg for the holidays, and the demonstration was again postponed, until late January.

"This isn't the end of the world, Colonel," Haeften tried to console Claus.

"Very nearly, my friend. Very nearly." Claus felt like a luckless Midas. Whatever he touched crumbled away into dust.

In spite of all the conflicting tensions, Claus was forced once again to wait. Christmas came that year shrouded in gloomy smoke and fog, with none of the old associations. Most shops were closed, and all were dark. The confectioners were boarded up. Streetcars, packed with weary workers, had their windows painted a funereal black. Their single light was ghoulishly blue, as were the street lamps. The churches where Christmas should have made a stand heard few carols but many confessions and frenetic prayers. At the park zoo, the crocodile was killed by a bomb and lay on his back for days, his teeth bared in a permanent grin. Bad weather no longer kept the Allied bombers away. They

Admiral
Wilhelm Canaris

used radar now, and their activities gave Berlin its only look of spurious gaiety. The burning buildings suggested brightly lit parties, but otherwise, Berlin had put out its lights.

All the while the Gestapo was at work. Count Moltke, who had devoted himself to planning a postwar Germany, was arrested. As had long been anticipated, Hans Oster had been taken into custody in December, 1943. Admiral Canaris had been dismissed and his arrest was expected any day now. The Gestapo were no longer to be underrated. They were bloodthirsty as winter wolves and as clever about pain as Chinese executioners. Most particularly, they were as tireless as spinning spiders. They had to spin to keep alive, and their webs were everywhere. Sickness, too, had taken a toll of the conspirators. Field Marshal Witzleben had fallen gravely ill and, though recovering, was out of touch with the plotters. General Beck was also recuperating from what had finally been confirmed as an operation for stomach cancer. Claus had visited General Beck in the hospital and later at his home. Though still devoted and keen of mind, Beck was old and exhausted, his strength perhaps unequal to the commanding task which would be his following the assassination of Hitler.

Meanwhile, the civilians among the conspirators clamored for action. Why didn't the Army do something? They had killed millions across the face of Europe, so why couldn't they dispose of one man? Claus attempted no reply. In fact there was little that winter which made for optimism. The only sane achievement he had observed was that of his brother Berthold who, as advisor on international law to the Ministry of Marine, managed to pass some American ships through the German blockade to bring food to the starving Greeks.

Before Captain Bussche could be recalled from Russia for the January attempt on Hitler's life, word came from the front that he had been gravely wounded. He had lost a leg, and so would hardly do for presentation before the Fuehrer.

The next assassination attempt had nothing to do with Claus, but he heard about it. A Colonel von Breintenbuch smuggled a pistol into Hitler's conference room, but felt himself so scrutinized by the Fuehrer and his SS guards that he never dared insert his hand into his pocket. The story only reinforced Claus's belief that a bomb was the only solution. With the winter uniform demonstration rescheduled for February, 1944, General Tresckow produced another recruit, Ewald Heinrich von Kleist, an infantry officer, the son of a conservative Pomeranian landowner. He visited Claus at Wannsee, slipping in quickly and quietly as one long practiced in the art of deception.

Claus examined the newcomer critically. A slender man, Kleist's face had an almost feminine softness except for his eyes. From them radiated a silent hatred which might be taken for the edge of insanity; the look of an animal brought to bay. Never still, these eyes examined every corner of the room. Claus suspected that Kleist had cracked up before, and would again.

"We're alone. I give you my word," Claus said.

"I had no thought to the contrary, Colonel," Kleist said, but still his eyes kept roving.

"You know what I have to ask you?"

"Colonel, you needn't ask." Kleist was the sort whose passions took the form of a rush of words. "When I think of that man, I bite my lips to taste blood. It isn't my blood, you see. It's his, Hitler's. I taste his blood. When I sleep, I dream of smashing him flat—arms, legs spread out, blood spurting from his fingertips. You look disturbed, Colonel Stauffenberg. I just want you to understand how much I've hated that creature every hour of every day for as long as I can remember. I hate him so much I will happily give up my own life for his death. Happily accept my doom if only I can witness his. I would rather go to hell with Hitler than alone to heaven. When I let this hatred loose, I'm almost overcome by it."

"You are aware that we will go down in history as traitors. Even if we succeed, there'll be little honor in it," Claus told him.

"I won't be a traitor to my conscience, Colonel. Do you remember the line from Goethe, 'The deed is everything, not the fame.'?"

Count Helmuth von Moltke, during his trial

"Then I can tell my people you're prepared?"

"You can, sir," said Kleist, leaning across the table to shake Claus's hand. "How soon?"

"We're hoping for the eleventh of February."

"Good. I can hardly wait," said Kleist, and there seemed a quality of predestination in his smile.

"And Kleist, before you go, let me suggest you get your hatred under control. We wouldn't want it to show."

But on February 11, 1944, Hitler's luck held good. An air raid canceled the uniform demonstration, and before it could be rescheduled winter was too far along to worry about a cold weather uniform. The project was called off. A bitter spring was upon the land. Only mud and the last shreds of winter ice held Russia back from the Polish and Rumanian frontiers. Claus's eye swept south on the map to Italy, then to Rome and a pin prick called Cassino. When that fell, Rome, the heart of Italy, would fall. Most threatening of all in its uncertainties, France stretched the length of his forearm on the map. There endless, raggedly protected miles of seacoast faced England and an invasion fleet, vast beyond reckoning, which awaited only the right weather and the best tides to strike. Time was the air breathed by the conspirators, and it was fast running out. "God knows we've tried," said Claus to Berthold. "We've had some brave beginnings but they always end in failure." If the Allied invasion of France came while Hitler lived, not only would it diminish what small chance Germany had to negotiate a peace, it would keep Field Marshal Rommel from turning his armies about to help in the coup d'état. Even without an invasion, Germany could not long support the manpower losses demanded by her war with Russia. Men were vanishing at the rate of one army corps a month.

Claus felt desperate now and desperation made him reckless. Almost every officer with whom he came in contact, as long as his reputation was not that of a convinced Nazi, was tackled immediately upon the conclusion of official business. "Let's get down to brass tacks," Claus would begin. "I'm carrying on high treason with all the resources at my disposal, and I need you to help." Never was he betrayed. Many were those who came over to the conspiracy, and some were ready to die for Hitler's death. Only the occasion was missing, and access to the Fuehrer. Hitler trusted no one except his dog Blondi, his mistress Eva Braun, and his personal staff.

While Claus and his fellow conspirators worked and waited with growing impatience, the Gestapo grew closer. The Gestapo were sheep, most of them, but sharp toothed and bloodthirsty. Woe betide the foe of such a flock. By April, 1944, resisters were being arrested at the rate of two hundred and fifty a day. The spring air was foul with fear and repression. When a Gestapo car went by, people fell silent whether they had anything to hide or not, for in Germany the accuser, not the accused, was sacred.

Each day had its share of evil portents upon which apprehension fed. Most disturbing of all, however, was word received through General Olbricht that Himmler and the Gestapo knew of a plot and were only leaving certain suspects at large to increase their final catch.

The car shuddered as it struck a deep rut. Claus came back to the present with a start. He looked at his watch—there was still time. His thoughts drifted back again.

Claus found himself brooding on his own security. Often it was loathsome to feel comparatively safe when asking others to take outrageous risks. At other times he would ask his aide, Haeften, if he felt capable of shooting him, in the event they were exposed. Claus felt certain he could not kill himself, but Haeften was not likely to be the answer either. One day he found his office in disarray, as though it had been clumsily burgled. That night he hurried home through the cold April rain like a fugitive, not from the bombs alone but from life itself. "I must get control of myself," he thought. For the first time he had had a row with Haeften in front of a quavering private and been proved wrong. "I'm wound up too tight. I can feel my spring beginning to go."

In mid-May he received from Stieff, who had long ago lost his nerve, a package of explosives and acid fuses. The glass fuses were pencil thin. It had been over a year now since his injuries, and the fingers of his left hand were unusually strong. With a small pair of pliers he managed, after several fumbling failures, to snap one of the fuses. He dared waste no more, but continued at odd moments to practice with the pliers, using wooden pencils as a substitute for the fuses. He had better success once he'd fitted the pliers' teeth with heavy rubber bands to prevent their slipping.

For the first time he realized he could, if necessary, do the job himself.

8

ON EITHER SIDE the forests, laden with late spring foliage, rose darkly above the small station. As the train backed out toward the main line, the evening sky was stained with oily black smoke from a green engine which seemed to shove the cars violently, resentfully. High above on the southern mountain slope the windows of Obersalzberg flung back the last sunlight. Hitler would be preparing for his evening of phonograph records. *Die Fledermaus* and something from Wagner, very probably. Claus had been at Obersalzberg, where Hitler had been conducting his afternoon staff meetings. He had not attended the actual discussion and now he was taking the train back to Berlin.

As the train gathered downhill momentum and the motion smoothed, Claus passed through the cars. June already, and he had still found no one to assume the role of assassin. He was looking for a Colonel Joachim Meichssner of the Army High Command Operations Staff. Meichssner frequented Hitler's staff meetings, and his derogatory statements about the chief of state had been quoted to Claus. It would be a desperate shot in the dark, but he had to try.

Claus found him sitting alone, a big man with cheeks as soft and fuzzy as the flanks of a cow. His jaw was oddly narrow; certainly not wide enough to contain thirty-two teeth.

"Colonel Meichssner, I believe?"

"Yes?" Already suspicious.

The train had gained the main Munich line by the time they

began their talk, and was making enough noise to mask Claus's direct inquiry. "May I speak in confidence?" he asked Meichssner.

"I'd rather you wouldn't." Meichssner smelled a rat somewhere.

"Why not?"

"Because the world is too much with us," he quoted mysteriously. "Look, Stauffenberg, I know about you. I even think I know what you want."

"I've heard your remarks about the Fuehrer quoted," said Claus. "They were far from flattering."

"Stauffenberg, is this a trap?"

"I wouldn't want to call it that. You have spoken in terms of, well, disposal, haven't you?"

"Yes, I have run off at the mouth at times."

"And you appear to be a brave man," said Claus.

"When I was a boy, Stauffenberg, I wanted to grow up to be the man shot out of a cannon at the circus. I was a very reckless and foolish child."

"Then what are all those medals for, Colonel Meichssner?"

"Drinking contests, Stauffenberg. Before each battle, I win a drinking contest. I am a brave drinker, but a cowardly soldier." By way of illustration he produced a bottle from his briefcase, pulling the cork with his teeth. "In battle, Stauffenberg, I imagine death in all its forms. My hands shake, my teeth chatter, even my hair is clenched. In Hitler's presence, I assure you, I'm a complete jelly, just like the rest of them. Just as you would be. Care for a bit of this? They say three drops on the tongue will send a mouse out in deadly search for a cat." He took a long pull at the bottle. "Didn't anyone ever tell you, Stauffenberg, never to trust a drunk? No matter what I might say now, when it came right down to it I'd drink myself silly."

"Stay sober now, will you, Colonel?"

"Why? Give me one good reason," demanded Meichssner.

"Because the world is dying, and you might give it life."

"Drunk or sober, Stauffenberg, I'm not suicidal."

"That's the point. There's a new sort of bomb with a ten-minute fuse. You simply put it in your briefcase in place of that bottle, set the case down next to Hitler and leave. You can be the savior of humanity and live to hear the applause."

"Escape Hitler's ant soldiers? I hardly think so."

"Come on, Meichssner. You're only having a bad day. We all have them. Let me put a little courage into you."

"No, thanks. I prefer this bottle. Stauffenberg, I can't help you."

"Germany needs your help."

"Feel my hand, Stauffenberg. Well, if you'd rather not, let me tell you it's cold and clammy. It's like touching the dead. I can't help myself."

"One need not be brave to have a sense of duty, Colonel Meichssner."

"Lord, the call of duty." He uttered a phlegm-padded cough. "Duty is so very German. What is it, anyway, but a sickness?"

"Colonel, try to pull yourself together."

"Stauffenberg, tell me candidly. Is your evident indifference to hazard because you've ceased to value life? I'm a whole man, myself. I don't want to give up one single finger for a principle."

"Until you've lost a hand," Claus said, "you can't imagine how precious the other one becomes. I have a lovely wife, delightful children. No, I have no wish to die. But tell me honestly how can any of us live in this country? Not with honor, surely."

"Hang honor, then."

"Meichssner, very soon France will be invaded. That will end any chance for a negotiated peace. The Allies will sow our country with salt. We must act before that happens. If I were in a position to do the job myself, or had anywhere else to turn . . . Meichssner, you're our one hope."

"No." Meichssner pointed his bottle like a pistol at Claus. "You're Germany's hope, not me. I prefer to keep myself of no interest to heaven and of no significance to hell. But you, Stauffenberg . . . Oh, I envy your talents, I really do, but I wouldn't want to be in your place. You're the one, three fingers and all.

You're the one who'll do it in the end. You're the only really dedicated one. The rest are damned cowards like me. You'd better believe it. I know the martyr type when I see it. You even look a bit like Jesus, Stauffenberg. Well, you haven't the rosebud mouth of the pictures, but I don't believe Jesus was like that. He must have had a stiff upper lip just like yours. And you have that manly, suffering look; that's what counts. It must be why it's so easy for you to get people to do things, Stauffenberg."

"I haven't had much success with you."

"You're making me drink out of shame. Listen, Stauffenberg, you have a lot of presumption to imagine you can be the savior of the German race."

"Don't, Meichssner. We haven't time for games. Fromm may come along at any moment now."

"And they'll crucify you. That's just what you want. They'll do it, and you won't save Germany, either. Christ didn't bring about a millennium, and neither will you. All he managed was a splendid job of dying. What a triumph! It's kept the poor church going ever since. Be sure you die well, Stauffenberg. You'll have every opportunity." He fixed Claus with red and bleary eyes, then jammed the neck of the bottle into his mouth. "Have you any idea," he said after he had swallowed, "what Hitler would do to me if he knew I were a drunk? The Russian front or Dachau, that's what. You won't report me, will you?" Claus shook his head. "You should have me shot for not going along with you. I'm a danger to you, but you won't, will you?"

"No. If we did that, we'd be just like them."

"If you really want to win, Stauffenberg, you should be more like them. You should be ruthless and a little mad. A successful leader needs a touch of insanity. Take Hitler. His assassin must be more like him."

At this point the train slowed sharply, then jumped ahead. Claus rose and went down the corridor. They were passing through the graveyard of a small village when the engine moaned a long, ghostly lament. It sounded like a shrill salute to all who lay dead or were about to die.

In the corridor, one car removed from Meichssner, Claus encountered General Fromm. The general looked like a big neutered cat, fat but still agile. Fat had formed pink cocoons around his bright boyish eyes. Fromm had been drinking, too; not to drown himself, but socially, in an ebullient beer-hall spirit. Fromm had had a good day.

"Ah, Stauffenberg! I thought I recognized your laugh."

"Actually, I haven't been laughing, General."

"Now's the time, Colonel, now's the time!" General Fromm was almost crowing with delight. "Stauffenberg, I want to thank you. Let me shake your hand." They went through the awkward ritual. "For the first time in over two years, the Fuehrer called me into his meeting. He was delighted, and it was your report, Stauffenberg, your report on the Reserve Army!" His round red face overflowed with the remembered pleasure of the Fuehrer's praise. For the moment Fromm's life seemed full and rich. "Guderian was there, too. He called you the best horse in the Reserve Army stable, Stauffenberg. I agree with him, Claus. You don't mind my calling you Claus, do you? There's a place for you at the head of my staff. I need a competent man."

"I have a rather heavy load already. What about General Olbricht?"

"Bother Olbricht. I have a new man coming along for him, a Colonel Herber."

Claus was startled. "Franz Herber?"

"Ah, you know him?"

"In Poland, yes."

Fromm's porcine eyes were confiding. "Think of it, Claus. You'll meet the Fuehrer face to face. The first time I met him, I discerned nothing out of the ordinary. Just one more wide-eyed politician, I thought, but I can't deny his greatness now. The man's a spellbinding genius."

The first few tears of rain trickled down the windows of the train, but Claus could not see them, for the glass was painted black. Although a berth had been set aside for him, he did not sleep well that night. Meichssner was forgotten. It was the possibilities in what General Fromm had proposed that frightened, yet drew him. He would have to go over it all with Olbricht as soon as they reached Berlin. That would be early in the morning, the sixth of June.

They met in Olbricht's Bendlerstrasse office at 9 A.M. The corridors resounded with noise; incessant ringing of telephones, slamming of doors, shouting voices gone shrill.

"Hysteria," Olbricht said. "It's been like this since six. Would you shut the door, Claus? That's better."

"You'd think it hadn't been expected all along," said Claus, feeling relief in a way that it had finally come, for events had totally eclipsed their concerns of the night before. According to all communiqués, the Allied invasion fleet had appeared off Normandy. It was said to have looked unreal in the first gray light of dawn, a ghost fleet formed of fog and thunder, flickering and terrible in its portent. All subsequent reports indicated that landings were being effected.

"Churchill must be puffing an especially fat cigar today," General Olbricht began. "And the Russians . . . let's not worry about them. They'll never pass the Pyrenees!" The jest brought no laughter. "Honestly, Claus, I have the nasty feeling the end of the race is in sight. I wonder if our conspiracy isn't over as well." He filled his pipe methodically, struck the match, put the pipe in his mouth and drew smoke thoughtfully. His hand trembled on the stem. "Anything we do now is apt to be taken as a stab in the back. We don't want that all over again. Perhaps Moltke was right. We'd better just wait it out and see what can be done with the ashes."

"I'd expect that of Goerdeler, but not of you," Claus said.

"I'll admit once one has decided on an objective it's hard to turn away, but Claus, my friend, circumstances have altered. Should we spill blood for nothing?"

"For nothing?" The possibility that this man whom he deeply respected was right overwhelmed Claus for an instant. Then he thrust the doubt aside. Granted that there was now no chance of a negotiated peace, but that never had been the real point.

Undeniably, the Allied invasion had hurt the chances for a successful coup d'état, but even in failure, if they shortened the war by one day, one hour, if they could give life to the innocent who would have died in that short time, it would be something. "My God, Friedrich, we have a duty as human beings to act against evil even if it's an empty gesture. It's the only way to keep from being part of it. It's the only honorable gesture we can make."

"We needn't argue theory, Claus. We've been all over that—honor, humanity, all those virtues and vices. Now we must decide as practical men, soldiers putting lives in the balance. Perhaps thousands of lives."

"Friedrich, I lay in bed last night. Do you remember how Conrad, in one of his stories, wondered why a spider had drowned in a particularly small ink well? Why, with all the choices in the world, it had ended there? Pure chance, divine purpose, why?"

"Who is this spider, Claus? You or me? Or Hitler?"

"Listen, I was just wondering if there was some sort of purpose in all this, in my being here, now, crippled as I am. When I was young I fancied being a farmer. I could swing a scythe as well as anyone in Lautlingen. But not better. Later on I meant to be a musician. I played well enough, but not really well. So I became a soldier. Though I'm not a bloodthirsty man, I think I was meant to be a soldier. I think now I was meant to be wounded."

"Don't be daft, Claus."

"Yes, I mean it, Friedrich," He leaned far over the table. "This ruined hand of mine—who would ever suspect? And what a chance. As General Fromm's chief of staff, I can issue orders to the Home Army in his name. More important, I'll have personal access to Hitler. It was meant to be that way all along."

General Olbricht listened attentively, his eyes expressionless. Not a muscle in his face moved. He did not seem surprised, nor did he apparently relish what he heard. "Yes, I know," he said.

"I heard first from General Schmundt. He feels Fromm is running out of gas and that you'll get the department moving. You made quite an impression on Schmundt. And I have a note here from Fromm to the same effect. I agree we could use you there, but Claus, no one can do this alone. One man can't coordinate a coup and be the assassin at the same time. It won't work. Besides, you're not the one to kill Hitler, not with your hands. Consider the facts afresh. We can't afford to lose you. Your place is here. I doubt the coup would go smoothly without you, Claus. Seriously, you sound like a man who wants to die. You aren't afraid to face the problems of the future, are you?"

Claus laughed. "I've never had time to get that complicated, Friedrich. It's simply that I seem to be the only one with the opportunity who's willing. Besides, you can manage here, you and General Beck."

"Beck's an old man in very poor health."

"I saw him the other day. Believe me, he's very resolute. And there's Goerdeler."

"Another old man with overactive glands. These prewars are as dead as Bismarck. It can't be left to the graybeards," said Olbricht.

"We don't seem to agree on anything today," Claus finally concluded. "The important consideration is whether we act now or go on procrastinating. Shall we toss a coin? It must fall heads or tails."

"Frankly, I don't feel like leaving the future up to the toss of a *Pfennig* and neither do you, Claus," said Olbricht.

"Then let's get Tresckow's opinion. You respect his judgment as much as I do."

"Agreed. I'll send von Lehndorff for him. Let it be up to Tresckow." They shook hands on it. "One last thing, Claus. This Colonel Herber who's supposed to take your place . . . he seems to know you."

"Yes, from Poland."

"He has all sorts of medals," Olbricht speculated, "but he

makes me uncomfortable. He has a face like a girl; makes him look a bit ruthless. Do you know he once chopped a turtle in half with a saber?"

"Where did you hear that?"

"Why, he told me so. He still seems amused at the idea. He was in the cavalry like yourself in the early days. He used to have burial detail. Said he could dig a horse's grave in under an hour as long as the legs and head had been cut off."

"He was always a little too efficient about following orders," said Claus. "Too literal. I had to demote him once. I wish now I hadn't. He may be difficult."

"Well, I won't have him in here," Olbricht decided. "I think if you're on the way upstairs, I'll get your friend Quirnheim."

"A good man, Quirnheim," said Claus.

"Herber will just have to fit into the arms section. There's an opening."

"Still," said Claus, "I wish he weren't around."

They broke off at this point. The situation in France demanded another conference at the Fuehrer's headquarters. General Fromm was in a rage. He had to report on the available reserves for the western front. "What reserves? What reserves?" he demanded, purple in the face, and in the end the burden of preparing a palatable brief fell to Claus. He spent the balance of the day and much of the night listing the skeletal divisions available in Germany and indicating at what rate they might be fed by convalescents and draftees.

At dawn Claus and General Fromm took a plane to Rossfelt, where a staff car met them. From Rossfelt the drive to Obersalzberg led through Berchtesgaden and then another fourteen hundred feet upward, back and forth over hairpin turns and forested roads, interrupted here and there with checkpoints and anti-aircraft batteries. Hitler's headquarters had grown from the small lodge of a radical politician into the romanesque fortress of a conqueror; barracks, gun emplacements, gas-proof shelters, and a sweeping view of mist-shrouded mountains, particularly the Untersberg. It was no accident that Hitler had chosen this vista of the mountain where Charlemagne was said to sleep. The conference itself was held in Hitler's oversized lodge. Fromm and Stauffenberg were shown in by one of several white-clad stewards, SS of course, their pistols discretely concealed. The carpets were so thick Claus had the sense of walking through a meadow. The walls were hung with medieval tapestries interspersed with vast paintings which exhibited masses of pink flesh and full bosoms. The furniture, too, was overgrown and stuffed, according to rumor, with the hair of Hitler's beloved dogs.

The briefing had already begun at a round table. The large picture window was open, giving an unimpaired view of the Untersberg together with a strong smell of gasoline from the garage below. Albert Speer, Hitler's Minister of Armaments, was speaking about his fears that a second Allied invasion might be attempted further to the east, on the North Sea coast, perhaps. Germany would be helpless unless the *Valkyrie* plan could be enlarged. In the echoing room, Speer's voice whispered as though through some vast organ pipe. He was urging the enlargement of the conspiracy without knowing it.

At first Claus thought Hitler was absent. Then he realized he was directly across the table behind a sheaf of papers which he held close to his face.

"In which case," the Minister of Armaments was saying, "we would be at their mercy."

"Speer!" The word seemed to ricochet off the walls. "In the first place," said the Fuehrer, his voice harsh, "the Reich is at no one's mercy. In the second, there are new weapons." He banged down the offending documents as if he wanted to push them through the table top. From his flaccid face, his eyes stared forth so intent and hypnotic that Claus seemed to feel himself being drawn forward; eyes so fierce they appeared to give off sparks.

When the tirade was over and victory again assured, Hitler came round the table, his hands locked together over his stomach. "Ah, Colonel Stauffenberg," he said, taking Claus's hand in both of his own. "You do excellent work. I have seen it. We will meet again." His glance had the force of a burning-glass.

"Yes, mein Fuehrer," was all Claus could manage as his heart seemed to shrivel within him.

A week later, while Stauffenberg and Olbricht were discussing the coup and its changing prospects, a sealed and coded message arrived from General Tresckow. It was brought in by Colonel Herber, or rather it appeared with him. Neither of them heard him arrive, but suddenly he was there, like some genie conjured out of the air and poised two feet within the open door. "A message from General Tresckow," Herber announced in a dry voice like a cicada sawing in the woods. "Top secret." His eyes seemed blue and honest as Lucifer's before the fall, but his smile was dangerous. He made a show of his departure, crashing his heels together, jutting out his arm in the Hitler salute so that his fingertips shivered.

"The military salute is quite sufficient here, Colonel," Olbricht told him coldly. "Thank you."

"Heil Hitler," replied Herber. He went out, closing the door unobtrusively behind him. They heard no footsteps in the hall, only a kind of odd laughter.

"Is that Herber?" said Olbricht.

"I don't know. Can he be listening?" Claus moved quickly to the door and looked both ways. "He's gone."

"He knows," Olbricht said.

"He doesn't know. He may suspect. I'll grant you he's a sinister sort."

"Probably educated by Jesuits. No matter, Claus. Let's see what our friend in the east has to say." Claus kept silent as Olbricht made his translation. He knew General Tresckow well enough to anticipate the contents, for it was not in the fiber of the man to turn back. Olbricht sat thoughtfully for a moment, then said, "Well, Claus, you win. I'll read it to you. 'The assassination must be tried at any price. Even if it fails, the attempt to grasp power in Berlin must move forward. We must show the world and future generations that the German resistance movement dared to risk even their lives. Compared with this, nothing else matters.' "

"Nothing else matters." Claus echoed the final phrase.

Olbricht turned away. "I hear you," he said softly. "You have won this time." Then he turned back, jabbing an emphatic finger. "But you can't win in the end."

"Perhaps not. But the world will know we tried. Whether we fail or not, it's a thing that must be done."

"Claus, should a few men presume to take on all the evil in the world? We can't suffer penance for all Germany, and there's nothing else if we fail."

"I'm not saying we can atone for all. But if there is a Germany after this war, where will it find even a shred of self-respect if we all go down to the last man with that monster? Friedrich, our children will deny us unless they can say, 'They weren't all like that.' "

"But Claus, think of the price. The disgrace, a painful death."

"It's worth it," Claus insisted.

"Is it? Wait until you're dead, and then tell me."

"Friedrich, that's our secret weapon—the willingness to die. And remember, it may not come to that." Except for one fierce determination, all else had become foreign to Claus. He cared little that he might commit mortal sin, that his life had become a tissue of treachery and lies. Nothing remained sacred, nothing but his savage resolve that Hitler must die.

"I pray you make it," Olbricht said.

"We will. As the Russians say, 'When God wills it, even a broom can shoot.' "

"Well, Claus, I'm glad you've kept your sense of humor. I've seen it ward off death before."

It might not work that way with death, but it helped with fear and doubt, which could so easily contaminate those with whom he worked.

"There's only one thing," Claus said. "Before I join Fromm's staff I must see Nina and the children." It would not be easy, but it, too, had to be faced.

On a fair afternoon in late June, Claus went home to Lautlingen, to his wife and children, and the ghosts whose nobility he cherished, not as privilege but as obligation. His coming was a surprise. The children leaped all over him while Nina waited patiently. Finally husband and wife clung together, more with relief than passion, a long-married embrace, deeply private.

"I'm crying, isn't that silly? I'm so happy to have you here that I'm dripping all over your uniform. Just like Pavlov's dog, whenever I see you, I cry." But in times of trial, he knew she was resolute, hiding a core of steel that had often surprised him in their younger days. Now he had come to depend upon it. They drew apart to consider one another closely, to judge what changes the months had made.

Nina ran a finger across his brow. "New lines. Dearest, you've been having a bad time."

"Nina, Nina, you are my lovely girl." He gazed long and intently into her eyes as though to store up a memory.

"What sort of a day have you had? What did you do?" she asked as though he were any businessman home from the office.

"I had a very dreary, tiring day until I arrived here."

"All days are that way now. Come, if you're not too tired, let's walk. It's lovely toward the forest this time of year."

And so they walked down the street of the old Swabian town. An old woman nodded to him, as she and her ancestors had to Stauffenberg lords and princes down the years. Claus nodded back, thinking, "I used to play with her sons. Now they're probably at war or dead. I don't dare ask." In the fields there were only the old men now. "They're good people, Nina," he said out loud. "These Swabians are the only freemasonry Hitler couldn't break down." Beyond the fields stood the forest, and the children darted ahead toward a dark green wall in which Hansel and Gretel might have lost themselves.

Claus and Nina walked slowly, silently, hand in hand until Nina said, "Have you noticed, Claus? I'm pregnant again. It's beginning to show."

He laughed aloud. "Well, they'll have to give you the Mother's Cross this time."

"Hush, it isn't funny."

"There, there." He gave her a pat on the shoulder.

"Don't treat me like a horse," she said, putting her hand to her hair where the breeze had ruffled it.

"I'd forgotten how lovely it is here," he said. Roses were everywhere, pink, white, red, the petals beginning to fall. "What will you do with so many roses?" On the lake, three swans turned as one without any motion of their tails or necks. They seemed to be attached to a submerged float and propelled from beneath. By a cluster of lily pads, husband and wife stopped to admire the goldfish, big fellows, some of them turning green and brown, the survivors of an age of luxury.

"At the rate things are going," Nina said sadly, "we'll soon be eating them."

The children came dashing back along the gravel path. They put a boiling in the air around them. Valerie had a winged maple seed affixed to her nose. "Look, I'm Pinocchio!" she shouted.

With difficulty, Claus lofted her up over his head. The boys pressed round him like so many eager puppies. He tried to lift them all. "Berthold, you're too heavy for an old man with only one hand."

"Children, your father isn't a toy," Nina said patiently. "Run ahead and pick us some flowers."

"How they've grown," Claus said. "It must be impossible to keep them in clothes."

"We manage."

Again they walked silently, following the shouts and laughter, but Claus had things he intended to say. He was too honest to harbor troubles for long. He liked them to be out in the open. Nina walked thoughtfully, knowing that he wanted to speak. In the end, she began it. "I know you aren't staying long, Claus. No, don't spoil it. Don't say how long. But this time I want to come with you to Berlin."

"Oh, Nina, you know how dangerous it is. The raids . . . it won't do for the children."

"I'll come alone, then."

"I couldn't work, Nina, thinking of the risk." She looked at him skeptically from under her brows in a way she had when she disbelieved what he said. "Well, yes, there's more. I don't know whether I should even tell you."

"I understand," she said. "You've found another woman."

"What childishness!"

She smiled ruefully. "I'd only hoped it was that simple." A cloud shadow drifted between them and the lowering sun. It brought a chill. The trees, all of silent listening nature, seemed to know and so did she. "I'm frightened, Claus."

"Of what?"

"Of what you're about to say."

"I don't want you to be frightened, Nina," and immediately he sensed these were scarcely words of reassurance. "I love you. I only pray I do not cause you pain with what's to come. The world has so much more hate than love these days."

A gust of evening breeze tossed back the children's laughter from a sunless and secret grove. "It is all so lovely," Claus thought. "What a marvellous place to grow old with one's family." He'd been a child here too, and a boy, trekking into the forests with Berthold, throwing spears at shadows as their ancestor Hugo von Stophenberg must have done eight centuries before when he marked out his claim to this land. This Stauffenburg land. Claus stood still. He stopped breathing, felt only his heart and his blood and the silent wilderness leaning over him with its breath also withheld, waiting, measuring him. Then the children, prancing back like carousel ponies, broke the spell. Wind stirred the leaves. A raven gave its call.

The children raced on again. He was alone with Nina once more, and he was afraid of her just then for it was within her power to destroy his resolve. No, it was not even his, except as a kind of trust passed down, any more than it had once belonged to Hugo, or would belong to his own children or their descendants yet unborn. "Nina, you must look at me." His voice was hoarse, a whisper. She did not seem to hear. "Nina, we have very little time." She turned now, biting her lip. "Nina, I must ask a great deal of you. More than I have any right." She nodded, understanding but not trusting herself to speak. "What if I were to tell you that Hitler is dead?"

"I wouldn't believe you, Claus. If that man were dead, I'd know. I think I could tell it from the bird song, from a new sparkle in the air."

"He must die, Nina. And there are those who would kill him."

"That man will decide his own time for dying, Claus. His type always does. Assassins only succeed in killing good men."

"I hope that isn't true, Nina."

"You're not trying to tell me it's to be you, Claus. Say it isn't you!" She was fierce now, fighting for her home. "Oh, God, how you men enjoy killing."

"Some men, perhaps. For me it's like running along the edge of a cliff, never knowing when I'll fall off."

"Yes, but it's exciting, isn't it?" she accused him. "Meanwhile, it's exciting. Admit it, Claus."

"Nina, please. Let's not quarrel. I don't want to hurt you. What I do want is a decent world for you . . . for our children."

"But what about you, Claus? Where will you be?"

"That I can't promise. I can only do my best."

"You aren't an assassin, Claus. You aren't."

"Nina, look again."

She raised her hands to her cheeks with growing realization. "You are. Why? My God, Claus, why?"

"Because Hitler is evil. It's as simple as that."

"There's no law against being evil."

"God's law, Nina."

"Then let God pull the trigger."

"God has had his chance. Nina, I can't live out my life in this sewer. What's far more important, I can't have my children growing up in it."

"A child without a father is no child at all."

"I'm no martyr, dear, but it's a necessary risk. With any luck, I'll soon be with you again."

"Can there be anything worth dying for in this despicable war?"

"Nina, can't you see you're making it harder for me? Can't you try to see why I must do this?"

"I can't, Claus. I never will."

"You've always lent me strength. Help me now to do what I must with a good conscience." In her eyes there was a look of animal incomprehension which he had never seen before.

"If you die, Claus, I won't promise to go on living. Not even for the children."

"Please, Nina."

"No, I can't make it easy for you. I almost lost you once before."

"Nina, without your support, I don't know how I can face what I must do."

"I'm speaking my heart, Claus. You may die in this business and never return. That's what terrifies me. I won't lie to you, Claus. If that happens, I will hate you."

He turned from her at last, his face distorted. "Dearest, please. Please don't."

Then from behind she threw her arms around him. He turned, still in her arms, and she raised her face to him with a searching movement of her eyes as if there were something he should notice, a truth beyond his truth. It lasted a long moment, and then she began to murmur so softly that he had to lean his head toward her. "I know you're like no other man in all the world. Why must you be the one to sort this out? But you will, if anyone can. You will." She buried her face in his chest and he held her close.

"Thank you," he whispered. "Thank you, dear Nina." Silently he stroked her hair.

The evening gathered itself. Golden, it arched over them, gilding the high mountain peaks, laying a last yellow blade of light in the pine tops. Some day, perhaps, he would set out early in the morning on the long hike to Felsentor, up through the beech forests with all the world below. Berthold was already old enough. What an adventure that would be, taking his sons. He felt strong again, strong enough to move mountains.

In the valley, a church bell chimed the hour, its bombilation blending and reverberating on the heavy summer air.

"It's humid tonight," he said.

"Is it? Perhaps there's a storm about. I've had the feeling all day." Nina shivered. "Let's find the children. I don't really want to go back. I wish we were rabbits. We could live in the forest."

"And the peasants would come and hunt us."

"I suppose so. It's a hungry time."

Dusk was quickly extinguishing the light and warmth of the summer day when Claus called the children. Pulling up their stockings, pushing back their hair, they came soundlessly over the needle-padded floor which stretched away into inky shadow.

On the way back, Nina asked, "Are you staying until tomorrow, Claus? Say you are. I want all of us to go to church together." He was silent. "It's the last thing I shall ask of you."

"Nina, I can't. I must go tonight. The car will be coming for me."

"And if I throw myself in front of this car, will you stay?"

"Yes, until they send another."

"I know. I know."

"I'll go to church in Berlin, Nina. That's a promise."

The car was not due until eleven. Dinner was a waiting time. Even the children sensed it and were silent. Berthold tried to sit on his father's lap. He was too old, but Claus allowed it, saying, "You're so big these days, I'll just have to hold part of you." The plates were cleared. Valerie was put to bed. Claus imagined the ancestors, the men in armour and plumed hats, glowering darkly

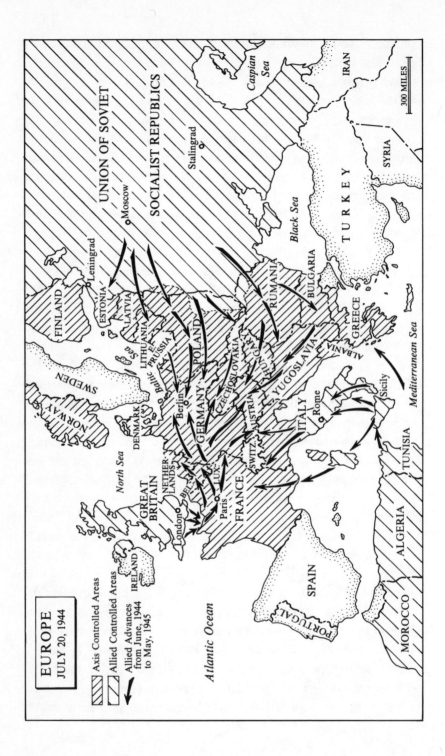

EUROPE
JULY 20, 1944

Axis Controlled Areas

Allied Controlled Areas

Allied Advances
from June, 1944
to May, 1945

300 MILES

UNION OF SOVIET
SOCIALIST REPUBLICS

Caspian Sea

IRAN

SYRIA

TURKEY

Stalingrad

Moscow

Leningrad

FINLAND

ESTONIA

LATVIA

LITHUANIA

EAST PRUSSIA

Baltic Sea

SWEDEN

NORWAY

DENMARK

Berlin

GERMANY

POLAND

CZECHOSLOVAKIA

HUNGARY

AUSTRIA

RUMANIA

BULGARIA

Black Sea

GREECE

ALBANIA

YUGOSLAVIA

SWITZ.

ITALY

Rome

Sicily

Mediterranean Sea

TUNISIA

ALGERIA

MOROCCO

SPAIN

PORTUGAL

Atlantic Ocean

North Sea

GREAT BRITAIN

IRELAND

London

NETHER-
LANDS

BEL.

LUX.

Paris

FRANCE

from the walls in silent satisfaction. The clock in the hallway ticked very loudly, louder it seemed than the sound of the staff car when it pulled up outside.

It was time to part.

A month had passed since then; a month in which battlefronts crumbled and thousands died in combat, under bombs, in gas chambers. It had been a month of alarms, rumors and bungled attempts at which the fragile web of conspiracy trembled, a month in which time was running out. Probably, thought Claus, the Gestapo knew everything and simply waited, the playful tiger with its prey. If they did not know, they soon would, for they had those who knew under drugs and under torture.

Every phone call Claus made might be bugged, every letter he received opened and read. Every time he left the office, it might be searched. Complete caution was impossible, and one evening in July, so perfect, the air so free of smoke that he could smell flowers, Claus chose to walk home with a briefcase full of papers more dangerous than the bomb itself. Once there, he paused on the sidewalk to enjoy the last golden feathers in the west when a black Volkswagen screeched around the corner and pulled up, jolting its front tire on the curb. Doors were flung open like great listening ears and two men leapt out. Gestapo! Claus braced himself. This was it, but they shouldered past him. It's a search, he thought, and he forced his mind to determine what evidence they might find in his rooms. Before he could decide, the men had rushed on to the neighboring building and burst open the door. Silence, then an inhuman scream. Battering blows. Silence again, and three figures emerging. The third was being dragged, head down, between the other two. "I don't know him. I don't know that man," Claus thought. "It's a mistake. That should be my blood on the sidewalk." The Volkswagen had closed its ears, the motor which had been left running gave a howl and the car bounded away.

Claus stood as though nailed to the cement, watching the

empty street. A film of icy sweat enveloped him. Anger, relief, fear, he felt them all, and something else that wasn't exactly weariness or regret. My God, he wasn't envying a man already in Gestapo hands? A man whose obligation to struggle was over? He must pull himself together. He looked up. The sky had gone completely black. He turned toward the house, his briefcase still intact, the tyrannicide before him, the anti-Christ still his to destroy.

"Still mine to destroy," Claus whispered to himself. The time had come and the presumption of such an undertaking weighed Claus down, filled him with a sense of unreality. He was a puppet worked on strings, an unrehearsed actor about to be thrust on stage, and yet his briefcase was real enough with its terrible weight, and the staff car was the same one in which he had visited Nina a month before. "Nina." He whispered her name. She was no more real now than a lovely vision left over from a forgotten incarnation. Thank God, she could not see him, pulling up to the Berlin airport. The hangars stood in silhouetted ranks against the sky. The plane, already rolled out, stood waiting, a silent gray dragonfly in the distance. Behind the low hills of the eastern horizon hung the hazy sun, red-eyed after the short night. It was 6:30 A.M., July 20, 1944.

9

CLAUS AND HAEFTEN, his aide, walked toward the waiting plane. It was an HE 111, single-engined and spidery, the property of General Eduard Wagner, Quartermaster General of the Army. Momentarily alone with his chief, Haeften wanted to know, "What are our chances, Colonel Stauffenberg? Will we make it this time?"

"I doubt it. Think of the odds."

"Then why? Why, Colonel?"

"Someone has to try, Haeften. My God, what a people we are, if no one even tries."

General Stieff, who had once guarded the explosives now in Claus's briefcase but who had lacked the courage to ignite them, was waiting beside the plane with his adjutant. Major Roll wished them all Godspeed, and then they were aboard. At 7 A.M. the engine sneezed out pale blue smoke. The pilot began pulling and depressing switches. The machine trembled, the glass vibrated, the seats shook. Chocks were pulled away, and they taxied into the thinning mist. A red sun flooded the cabin as they turned around. They moved to the end of the runway. Then the plane leapt forward as though it had been kicked, and they sped toward the bleeding oval of the sun. Along the horizon, the black jagged teeth of the city became visible as the tail elevated. Then the windscreen tilted lower to reveal Berlin's blackened ruins. Vibrations diminished as the earth relinquished its grasp. They were aloft into a new day over Germany. Ears became ac-

customed to the whistle and pound of the propeller. Rastenburg lay three hundred and fifty miles to the northeast over the Prussian plains.

Little conversation competed with the wind and the beat of the engine. Claus leaned back and tried to rest his body and mind for the task to come. He made his body relax, but thoughts

Julius Leber (LEFT),
during his trial

crawled through his mind like hungry crabs. So much had happened in these last weeks; so much had changed. An important ally, Major General von Rost, Chief of Staff in the Berlin military district, had been transferred to Italy, and now was rumored dead in action. His successor in Berlin, Major General Herfurth, was an unshakable Nazi. This severely crippled the command structure that was to carry out Operation *Valkyrie*. Of more recent and personal hurt to Claus was the arrest of Julius Leber, whom more and more Claus had come to favor over Goerdeler as future head of the civilian government. "We need Leber. We must get him out," had been Claus's immediate reaction. But there was no getting him out, and, in the two weeks that had passed, his focus had shifted from the desire to free a friend to speculation upon the degenerating effects of torture and drugs. Julius Leber knew too much. The disposition of all the figures on the chessboard of conspiracy was threatened by his captivity.

"If I fail today," Claus thought, "we are all finished." There had been too many failures already for the conspiracy to endure another. Twice before in the last few years decent men had primed themselves to take action; first under Beck and his general staff during peacetime, then again with Beck, Tresckow and the men of the *Abwehr*. Both times the moment to strike had come and gone, and the conspiracies had lost strength and direction. Now it was Claus's turn to take the irrevocable step. Already he was late in doing so. The conspiracy had passed its peak of readiness, and everywhere were signs of loss and decay. Affairs at both fighting fronts, east and west, offered no brightening prospects. In the east, according to the reports which Claus had studied, the armies were in virtual collapse. Even had they been holding firm, Tresckow and Olbricht had made no progress in dealing with their Nazi commanders, Schorner and Model.

In the west, from which Beck hoped for so much help, doubts had now cropped up. "Stuelpnagel's a good man," thought Claus. "If only we had more like him. If only we hadn't lost Rommel." Field Marshal Rommel, who had seemed so indestructible in North Africa, had been cut down by an English plane. He lay now as Claus had lain, hospitalized, between life and death. For expressions of pessimism, von Rundstedt had been relieved of his command and replaced with Field Marshal Kluge, Tresckow's old commander. "If only Tresckow had gone with him to the west," thought Claus unhappily. Tresckow knew how to handle the irresolute Kluge. Now it was all up to Beck. When the time came, Beck would have to try to win over Kluge and his western armies by telephone. Saintly, weary Beck, who coughed apologetically into his handkerchief. Claus feared for the old general's strength and for his ability to project it over a thousand miles of telephone cable. In truth, he had grave doubts about them all, including himself; perhaps himself most of all, and now those doubts were compounded. "Please God, we must succeed this time. As the Americans say, three strikes and out." He'd had two already.

On July 11, just nine days ago, he'd had the chance to nip the war, if not in the bud, at least in its full and dreadful flower, and he had not taken it. On the preceding day, after having been General Fromm's chief of staff for less than two weeks, he'd been ordered to a conference in Hitler's eagle's nest at Berchtesgaden high in the Bavarian Alps, to report on the condition of the Reserve Army. Claus had conferred first with Generals Stieff, Olbricht and Beck. It was a day of military disaster. A two hundred and twenty mile gap had been torn through Army Group Center in the east. Beck expected the Russians to enter Berlin within the month. In the west, the armies were being bombed into oblivion. What use was a conspiracy now? Claus's determination had narrowly prevailed, and it was decided he would take the bomb with him the following day, using it only if both Hitler and Himmler were present. Since their hold on the armies in the west had become more tenuous, they feared Himmler and his SS more than ever.

Haeften was ill on the eleventh, and Captain Klausing took his place as Claus's aide. They went by plane to Freilassing airfield, then by car to Obersalzberg. There, Claus had instructed Klausing to wait at the wheel.

"And, Sir," the captain had asked, "if I hear an explosion and you don't come out . . ."

"Pray, Klausing." Then, through his own fear, he saw the reflected fear in the young captain's eyes. "I'm sorry. I'm asking more of you than of myself. Just to sit and wait—that's the hardest thing. But not to worry. I'll come out. I'm going to get a lot further than this car."

Then Claus had climbed out of the automobile with his bomb-weighted briefcase. SS guards, as brutish and tough looking as a pair of bulldogs, stood on either side of the entrance. He passed them with a brisk step. Officers stood in stiff, cold groups in the long narrow hall. He weaved through them. His extremities were going cold as his heart beat picked up. There was a pain in his stomach. Presently he would begin to sweat as fear oozed through him, an alarming sensation which he tried to control. His animal parts seemed to be getting the best of him.

As Claus forced himself to the conference table, General Guderian was speaking mildly of the present disappointments in Russia. Even this old tank commander had learned to temper his words. Hitler heard him out, but his silence was as electrically charged and potentially explosive as a lightning bolt. It didn't last long. "General Guderian, from what you say, there appear to be two possibilities. Either we retreat or we renew the attack. Gentlemen, I do not propose a retreat. We must find out who is at fault and rectify the situation." Blame had to be fixed, a scapegoat found, and for all the Knight's Crosses winking up and down the table, for all the pain and death these men had faced, none dared suggest that the defect lay with Hitler. Few, it occured to Claus, even thought it. Accusations were hurled back and forth. Claus listened, his sweat drizzling to the surface. He had to spell out each word to make any sense, and the words put together were without logic. He had to force himself to remember why he was here. The bomb . . . he must look for Himmler. Even this was an effort. He was like a man trapped under a capsized rowboat, afraid to dive deeper in order to get clear. Himmler should be easy to identify, a tall man with plump cheeks and tiny, receding chin, big ears, steel-rimmed glasses, long wrinkled neck. From the back, Claus at first mistook General Jodl for the SS leader; wretched Jodl, who was jealous of Hitler's dogs. On command, it was said, he would lie on his back, arms and legs in the air, for a pat from his Fuehrer's hand. Jodl wasn't worth killing, and Himmler wasn't there. So much depended on this. Claus had no right to make a mistake.

Again he measured the silent faces, all of them fear struck and entranced. Only General Guderian was half smiling, as though he'd heard it all before. This second check confirmed the first, so Claus excused himself. He effected a walk of measured thoughtfulness which lagged behind his racing mind. From the switchboard, he put through a lightning call to Olbricht. They spoke in a kind of code, these two men who were risking their lives to speak at all. The decision was to postpone. Claus put down the phone. He had confronted doom itself, but that doom had looked at the calendar and said, hold on a few days, then we'll get together once more. With his pulse beating in his ears, Claus withdrew into a green tiled bathroom where he splashed

General Alfred Jodl

water on his face. He felt sick with relief, but he had a report to deliver. He must master himself and return.

Hitler was still bullying his staff. Claus had not been missed, though the tirade ended as he returned to the table. Hitler had worn himself out. He was panting like a winded horse, but just as swiftly as he had unleashed his wrath he produced a smile. "Now, gentlemen, please continue with the discussion. Today the good General Guderian has won a battle." The whole atmosphere eased. The Fuehrer was displaying his human side, the side that loved dogs, opposed vivisection, and posed with blond-haired toddlers for Christmas cards. It was a fraud, Claus knew. From a distance, in his silver-trimmed uniform, hands clasped over his paunch and his cap drawn down over his forehead, the dictator could pass for a streetcar conductor. But from the fleshy face with its great peg of a nose, eyes looked forth which seemed born of no woman, eyes without the memory of song or childhood. In Claus's imagination those ruthless eyes belonged to an implacable immortal who derived his only solace from the ritual sacrifice of his dying race. Could he really be killed? Would he return in another form? Was there always a Hitler waiting to be born and worshipped? These were not questions Claus dared ponder. He must strike even though, hydra-like, two heads grew for every one lopped off.

A three-day respite followed; three days of doubts, fears, reappraisals, and a meeting in the basement apartment of Elisabeth and Theodor Struenck in Berlin. The meeting was already well along when Claus arrived. Theodor Struenck was talking. He looked haggard, a man who had hosted conspiracy too long. As he talked he twisted a big gold ring on his left hand; but it wasn't a magic ring, for no genie appeared.

Doctor Hans Gisevius, Goerdeler's contact man in Switzerland, who had just returned to Germany to take part in the plot, said he as well as Goerdeler agreed that the bomb plot should be abandoned; they should rely solely on the so-called Western Solution, which anticipated better treatment from the conquering British and American armies than from the Russian forces. With this in mind, the German high command in France would initiate a surrender to the Anglo-American forces, while sending all available troops to bolster the sagging eastern front against Soviet troops.

"And how, may I ask, do you move these generals to act?" Claus asked him.

"If you could arrange for Goerdeler to talk with Field Marshal Kluge and the others . . ."

"My dear Doctor Gisevius, not everything can be talked."

"Nor can everything be done with a bomb, Colonel Stauffenberg. If you fail, the best of Germany's future leadership will be wiped out. I don't believe you have a right to take such a risk. You're being irresponsible with too many lives."

"It's my life, too."

Would anything ever happen, Claus wondered? How often they had made plans—a dozen, a hundred times—and revised them while all the clocks in Germany ticked and bombs fell, while the war nibbled away at so many lives, at all their nerves. It was not enough to say, "It's my life, too," for it would mean all their lives, possibly the lives of hundreds he did not know. The innocent would fall with the guilty, if killing Hitler fit such terms. And Nina, and his children . . . it was the sort of ruinous speculation he dared not indulge privately, much less admit aloud.

"I'm weary of sitting in cellars poking holes in the air with my fingers," he told them. "I'm willing to stake my future on this."

"It's not much of a wager," Gisevius interposed. "If it were only your future, Stauffenberg . . ."

"Doctor, it's too late for you to come from Switzerland and tell us to throw up our hands, to pull the covers over our heads. It's too late to make another plan. You won't move Kluge or any of the other oath-ridden generals until Hitler is dead."

"You sound like a fanatic, Stauffenberg!"

"I'm not deaf, Doctor Gisevius. And it's a small room."

"Damn it, Stauffenberg, I'm only giving you my opinion."

The room was stifling. Perspiration burned under Claus's eye patch and he dabbed at the pain with a wad of cotton. "Listen," he said as patiently as possible, "you don't even know I'll set off the bomb at all."

"Then why else are you here?"

"Why else? The point is, I will or I will not. But whatever, it's up to me now, and has nothing to do with all this shouting. Can't we open a window?"

"It is open," his host replied apologetically.

"It's like being in a killing box. Bricks and more bricks."

As if in answer to his words there was a loud cracking sound. Falling debris that had been loosened by a raid? They all sat very still, listening. There was no secret exit. The silence lengthened. Finally Struenck reassured them. "Listen, the whole place is falling apart." He rapped on the wall. "Hear that? Every bit of it's cracked. I think the paint is all that holds it together."

Claus was weary of rooms thick with smoke and indecision. For better or worse, the plan was set, and more talk could only weaken their purpose. The bomb was everything now; the bomb and the will power to give it life in Hitler's presence. With a sudden physical need to leave this room, to get into open air and breathe again, he rose from his chair. "Sorry about my temper," he said to Doctor Gisevius. "I've had a bad day."

"Not at all, Colonel. It's just that I have a feeling we'll never succeed."

"Nonsense. Everyone feels that way in wartime."

"I assure you, Colonel, I'm not speaking through fear. But I have a feeling very few of us will be alive this time next year, regardless of what happens with your bomb."

"Perhaps, Doctor. Perhaps we won't meet again. I'm not a pessimist, so let me leave you with this advice. Learn to smile, Doctor. Learn to smile." And then Claus was in the open air, filling his lungs and trying to shake off the tension that had gripped him in the close air of the basement room.

That was July 14. A conference with Hitler was scheduled for the following day. In the interim, the Fuehrer had moved his headquarters from Berchtesgaden to East Prussia. That was one difference. With time running out, the other difference was that Olbricht and Beck had decided that Himmler's presence was no longer a requirement for planting the bomb. Hitler alone must die. Claus had been obliged to prepare a sheaf of papers. Should Hitler be absent from the staff meeting, Claus would have to deliver a report on the gray-faced men and boys who came from ill-lit offices, who limped and coughed, who had rheumatic hearts: the troops of the Reserve Army. If Hitler were there, as expected, he might be called upon at once to report, with the unexploded bomb breathing at his side. In any case he would need the report as camouflage, as an excuse for reaching into his briefcase when the moment came to snap the fuse.

General Fromm accompanied Claus to East Prussia. They flew to Rastenburg from Berlin, arriving at half past nine in time for breakfast at the officers' mess and a discussion of manpower replenishment for combat areas. Afterwards, Claus talked with Generals Stieff and Fellgiebel to make sure all, particularly the communications section, was in readiness for the coup d'état.

The early afternoon conference took place at the reinforced Speer bunker. Hitler's own bunker was being renovated. Uncertain as yet of Hitler's presence, Claus had not started the acid fuse before entering the room. The Fuehrer was there, all right. Half-monk, half-soldier, he seemed to single Claus out. He walked toward him in an odd, ladylike fashion, one shoulder cocked higher than the other. Perhaps Claus was his ideal of a battered warrior, bearing wounds like medals for heroism. Perhaps, like the moth, he was attracted to the flame. The Fuehrer made a point of shaking hands. Claus had to put the briefcase down between his legs.

"My dear Colonel Stauffenberg."

"Mein Fuehrer."

Really, there was nothing to the man. He was short, hollow-chested, round-shouldered. His hair, parted down the center, was spotted with dandruff, but as always there were the eyes and the voice to contend with. Eyes more black and treacherous than death itself bored into Claus. He felt like a bug being scorched

At Rastenburg: Claus von Stauffenberg (LEFT)
with Hitler and unidentified officers

under a lens. "He knows," Claus thought. "He knows. His eyes are telling me that he knows everything."

"Well, Colonel, we must get busy. I have to hypnotize Quisling this afternoon. He's sagging a bit."

The conference got off to a bad start with General Jodl reading aloud a report from Rommel which concluded, "The troops are fighting heroically everywhere, but the unequal struggle is nearing its end. I must beg you to draw the political conclusions without delay." The staff was thunderstruck. Hitler sat limply, his unguarded right hand quivering as though approving the statement. Only the eyes remained alive and on fire. When Jodl put down the paper, there came a sudden change as though Hitler had been plugged into an electric circuit.

He stood up, stiff as a javelin. With a great gasp of indrawn air, he began to preach, assaulting them like a division chaplain. Not a word was uttered in contradiction as his voice climbed the register, gaining power and fury with every syllable. His listeners stiffened as the unleashed fury hit them like Wagnerian music and sent their minds reeling. The voice was a tremulous whisper, a growl, a croon, a bark. Claus listened with awe. His lips began to move in silent unison with Hitler's. There was one horrendous oratorical pause. Hitler swayed, his tongue seemed too large for his mouth. Then he was off again, and the pens and pencils danced on the table. They had heard from Rommel; very well. But Rommel was a defeatist. Rommel was ignorant and evidently a coward. Rommel had no knowledge of the new weapons even now being readied: rockets which would turn England into a wasteland, jet fighters so fast they had to fire backwards for fear of overtaking their own missiles.

As suddenly as it had been turned on, the current was cut off. They had been given their measure of courage and conviction. Let the meeting proceed with confidence. Hitler sat back, his hands locked at his waist. The generals began making their reports, and Claus had done nothing. He felt paralyzed and an icy sediment of fear seemed to have numbed his mind as well as his limbs. He tried to walk, but his muscles at first refused.

He was like a rabbit transfixed by the headlights of an oncoming car. After taking several deep breaths he managed to bow from the waist. "Will you excuse me?" No one seemed to notice. A large map had been spread on the table and the generals, including Fromm, were leaning over it.

Once in the long central corridor he went first to the switchboard and put through a lightning call to the Bendlerstrasse headquarters. He wanted to speak with Olbricht, who would set *Valkyrie* in motion once the assassination had taken place, but Olbricht was unavailable. Claus's aide, Haeften, answered. Neither Himmler nor Goering were present at the meeting, Claus explained. Should he proceed? Haeften answered with dumb silence. Were such questions still at issue? In any event, they had never been his to decide. Finally Haeften's voice at the Berlin end of the line said, "Colonel Stauffenberg, the orders calling for *Valkyrie* went out two hours ago. All has begun here."

"I just wanted to make sure," Claus replied. "Good. I shall proceed." He hung up, aware for the first time of his own confusion and filled with horror at his blundering. There was no reason for him to have left the conference table, no reason for the phone call except fear, and fear was no excuse. Alone in the corridor, he rummaged in his briefcase, put fuse and pliers together. There. It was done. The bomb was alive and breathing now. He hurried down the hall, slowing to a judicious walk as he entered the conference room, only to find that Hitler had gone. The generals, aroused by their leader's polemic, were left alone, warriors reborn, fashioning paper victories out of mud and blood defeats.

"Stauffenberg! What are you doing, bobbing in and out like a jack-in-the-box? You're making a spectacle of yourself." It was Fromm, his face a bright sunset hue.

"My apologies, General Fromm. I was ill. My wound . . ."

At his side, the acid was already gnawing away.

"You are pale," said the general. "You shouldn't come when you're not well. Makes a bad impression."

"If you'll excuse me, then . . ."

"Half an hour, Stauffenberg. Be at the car."

Alone, Claus bolted the lavatory door behind him. He turned the resisting faucet, let icy water penetrate the bomb. The cold on his wrist sank in, controlling his confusion of mind. Fumbling, his papers and his trousers sprinkled with water, he managed to extract the half-eaten fuse from the package of explosives. Then he turned to the wall and pounded his hand against it. His throat ached with the sob of rage he dared not utter.

Five minutes later he emerged, looking spruce if somewhat damp. It was one-thirty in the afternoon when he put in another lightning call to Berlin. This time he was able to reach Olbricht. Another failure. *Valkyrie* must be countermanded. Fortunately it was still in an early stage, with no commands having gone out which could not be explained as part of a training exercise. Claus felt a furious anger at the relief his body knew. He'd held Hitler's life in his hands and he'd permitted that monster to unman him. He'd been given that chance, and he'd squandered the opportunity with a needless telephone call. At the very least, more precious time had been lost and suspicion aroused. Thus he returned to Berlin with something worse than sin on his conscience.

The following day Claus met with Generals Beck and Olbricht. Olbricht was clearly upset by the fiasco of the day before, but the older general, who had tried his best for so long, showed the polite concern of an old gentleman whom nothing can disturb. He had fought a desperate illness successfully. It had taken a toll which pride could not entirely overcome. "Don't blame yourself, Colonel Stauffenberg," he said. "We all have regrets in this business, but we can't afford to dwell on them."

"General Beck, you wouldn't have failed twice."

"No, because I know myself too well to have made the attempt. We're none of us tyrannicides by nature, Colonel. You've forced yourself to the brink, and I respect that. Next time you'll succeed."

But failure had cost more than time. "Field Marshal Keitel is suspicious," Olbricht said. "We won't be able to disguise *Valkyrie* as a training exercise again. The next time we must launch the coup regardless of what happens at the Fuehrer's headquarters." He looked at the others. They nodded in agreement. "Now, General Beck, can we count on Witzleben to act promptly?" Beck nodded. "And Kluge?"

"I believe Kluge is aware of the realities in the west. I think we can count on him once Hitler is dead," replied General Beck. Then he said more reflectively, "He's a strange man, Kluge. Did you know he once challenged Guderian to a duel and asked Hitler to be his second? Hard to believe, isn't it? I don't like his denying Tresckow a posting to his headquarters. He might get cold feet again, although I doubt it, once Hitler's actually gone."

"Then there's Fromm."

"I don't know Fromm, really."

"I've spoken to him very frankly," said Claus. "He knows my views and he usually says, 'Very interesting,' and gives me a Heil Hitler. Yet he's never done anything to expose us."

"Except for his rank, he's nothing," said General Beck. "You could pick him up by the dozen in any railway station. The question now, gentlemen, is do we proceed? I'm a soldier of the old school, and I know how many lives this is apt to cost." He sagged forward like an ancient horse abruptly freed from the shafts. "I feel that the great moment for the coup d'état is gone forever. We can no longer hope for a settlement with the British and Americans, but gentlemen, our moral duty remains; a call of honor." His body was wracked, but his spirit and his resolve were unshaken. "That is my feeling, but it's not for me to make the decision. In any case, I'm near the end of my days, and for me it's not such a risk. I shall have two revolvers in my pocket and nothing to fear. The decision belongs to you, Colonel Stauffenberg."

July 17 was a day filled with unpleasant revelations. Russia had launched yet another offensive. An arrest order, long anticipated, had been issued for Goerdeler, but the worst news was that about Rommel, felled by a British fighter plane and now lying in Saint Foy de Montgomery in France with a triple skull fracture. If not lost to life, he was lost to the conspiracy, and with him the devoted troops who, under his command, might well have insured the coup's success. The dreary day ended for Claus when a late night *Wehrmacht* radio communiqué concluded with the statement, "The population has sustained grave losses." When this was immediately followed by a recording of the song, *Another Beautiful Day Draws to its Close,* Claus began to laugh and was still laughing helplessly when he fell asleep.

July 18 brought more calamitous news, which this time left him dumbfounded. A naval officer named Kranzfelder, a friend of his brother Berthold's, informed him a rumor was abroad that within the week Hitler's headquarters was to be blown sky high. According to Kranzfelder, this was public knowledge, but beyond that he could not elaborate.

That night Claus worked on a report concerning the Volks-grenadier Divisions. The report was to be submitted to Hitler within forty-eight hours, on July 20, at Rastenburg. So the day was set. It remained for him to make the final decision, but how? The plan sounded all right among friends around a table at night, but tomorrow and the day after, in broad daylight among enemies, how good would it be then? What chance was there that the bomb would fail? It had before. What chance that, if it exploded, it would not kill? Step by step each possibility seemed good, better than even, but putting all those fearful "ifs" together. . . . Claus was no statistician, but he knew. If only they could rely upon a loyal and disciplined army to act, but there were just the tenuous threads of honor holding the aging men of the conspiracy together. They were all afraid. God knows he'd proved himself irresolute and frightened, too. He could not delude himself there. "I'm ready to die," he told himself, "but after the deed is done. To die before would be pointless." This was his resolved self thinking. At other moments his weaker nature asserted itself and he lapsed into despondency. He would never find the courage to set off the bomb. He'd have to find someone else. Better yet, he could snap the little fuses and throw the explosive into a bomb crater, have done with it. That was infantile protest, like banging the crib bars with his head or putting a pistol in his mouth as young Werther had done. Damned if he'd let people despise him as a suicide if any other choice remained. They said prussic acid was a pleasant way to go, just a little giddiness and then death amidst the aroma of peach blossoms. Not strychnine. He'd heard it produced terrifying paroxysms, the victim practically turning himself inside out in the process. He had to consider these possibilities calmly, rationally, in case the assassination attempt failed, for he could not then remain alive to incriminate his friends.

It was lunchtime on the nineteenth of July when Claus left his office on Bendlerstrasse, and drove to the cavalry school at Krampnitz. He had not ridden since he had been wounded, but the commanding officer, Colonel Momm, was an old friend. He said nothing about the missing hand when Claus asked him for the loan of a difficult horse.

"Good," said Momm. "I'm glad you've come back." Then, without further comment he produced a horse with a small head and nostrils slanted like a stag's. The animal quivered and his ears went back as Claus mounted. They were off like the wind with a heavy undulation of life untethered. "I'm riding," he thought with delirious satisfaction. "I'm actually riding again." Before he dismounted he had the horse responding to the touch of his knee, the hint of a wrist. In one spot they managed to execute the cadenced trot which was called a *piaffe*.

"I feel better," he thought. Maybe he was not the rider he had been, but he still could control a horse. In an odd way this ride fixed his last resolve. If he'd been thrown, then presumably he would have been unfit for travel to East Prussia the next day. A good fall might have put him out of action indefinitely. As it was, he had exposed himself to Providence and not been found wanting. Maybe he would win no final victory, maybe he would die in the attempt, but it was something he was destined to face, and this awareness put out the last fear.

That evening there remained one obligation. He had promised

Nina that with the time remaining he would do what he could for the sake of his soul.

The sun was setting over Berlin when Claus entered an ancient church which had somehow survived in an area of destruction. Inside were stone and marble tombs of old warriors and statesmen asleep under their shields and banners with stone dogs curled at their feet. Bone fragments of forgotten saints reposed under glass and jewels. In a small side chapel, Claus knelt, shut his eyes, and let the darkness enter his soul. He felt like an infiltrator in a land from which he had been exiled. Somewhere a hushed voice chanted as though casting a magic spell.

Claus rose. His eyes had now grown accustomed to the dark and he noticed in a gloomy recess the towering mural of a saint, crucified upside down. The saint's face was composed, even smiling, despite the posture and the blood. He must either be dead or very sure of paradise. Claus was still confronting the painting when a voice from behind him said, "My son, may I help you?" He turned to see a tall, wintery priest with a greyhound's face, the flesh drawn tightly back to lobeless ears as though it had been surgically lifted. Rainbow tints from a stained-glass window above tattooed him in garish patterns.

"Father, I've come to confess."

The priest turned back each wide sleeve of his surplice with an elaborate gesture. "Very well, my son. Follow me."

While waiting for the priest to enter the confessional, Claus tried to pray. No words came. He wanted a miracle; Hitler dead of a lightning bolt. Leaning back, eyes closed, he tried the Lord's Prayer. It rested on his tongue, dead and unsavory as a rusty nail. He couldn't concern himself now with daily bread, but at last other words began to come. "O God, if there is punishment, let it be mine alone. Spare my family and help them to understand. Spare the others. They're all good men. Germany will need them. It can do without soldiers like me."

The slide clicked open. The outline of the priest's face formed at the grating in profile, resting upon his hand.

"When did you last confess, my son?"

"I can't remember."

"Weeks?"

"Longer."

"Half a year?"

"More than a year, Father." So much time had been wasted. They'd torn off all of 1943, and the first six months of this year plus nineteen days of July. Torn them from the calendar of duty and balled them into the wastebasket; ruined days like wingless moths. "I've doubted the existence of God, Father. I've thought that in our fear and doubt we make an image and call it God."

There was a prolonged silence. The priest breathed heavily through his narrow nose. "We all of us have doubts," he said. "Perhaps in these times I have more than you. It is a test of our faith which we must not fail."

"I have thought to take a life, Father."

"Killing is a sin, my son."

"Isn't it a greater sin to fail to act through cowardice? God wouldn't think better of me for sparing this man because I am afraid. This man is the anti-Christ, Father. He's betrayed his people."

"Not at all, my son. If we are speaking of the same one, he has always kept his promises."

"Then it is the German people who have betrayed themselves."

The priest was first to use the name. "Hitler never lacked the courage to do evil. The rest of us have been too cowardly to do good."

"Then he must die, Father."

"Die, perhaps, but by murder? Life is a priceless gift, my son. It is the result of divine purpose. Even Adolf Hitler was placed on earth for a reason, just as the scourges and pestilences of old. You, too, perhaps. You may be here to end that scourge. It is not for me to say."

"Surely, Father, it's not a mortal sin to kill such a tyrant."

"Perhaps. Perhaps if all other means have been tried and have failed. He who kills a tyrant must be sure of the agreement and silent support of the majority of his people."

"Surely there is that support."

"I hear many confessions. Many would surprise you." When the priest spoke again, his focus seemed to have shifted. "My son, if you question God, do you question damnation as well?"

"I've never had the self-assurance to believe in nothing, Father."

"And hell . . . does it exist for you?"

"It does."

"I am not concerned about your body, my son, which must eventually die, but about your soul. You must think of your soul, which may endure torment throughout all eternity. You believe in that sort of hell?"

"I was taught about fire and brimstone as a child."

"And you believe?"

"Not exactly. For me, hell would seem to be an everlasting sense of failure."

"I see."

Both were silent a space. Then Claus said, "Will the Church give me absolution?"

"It cannot, my son. It cannot." The priest's voice was husky; it seemed about to break. "Once the Church held this land together. It held it together and made it great, but for years I've stood silent, watching my parish sink into nothing, vanish away. I've never been so terribly aware of my people's helplessness, and mine. I cannot speak for the Church, my son. I cannot officially condone thoughts of homicide. But I will pray for you, in your labors of the days to come. I will pray for your soul."

His confession was at an end. He had done that much for Nina. Stepping from the dark sanctuary into the street again, he saw the harsh details of the world at war. There God vanished like a burst soap bubble. Yet he had come from a people whose lives were full of God. Now Germany seemed to have lost God, and he, for one, was learning to fill his life with man. He considered writing Nina, to tell her he'd been to confession. Better no contact just now; better not even the making of a will which, if he failed, would not be honored anyway. He pondered the report he might have to make before Hitler while the bomb's fuse was being eaten away. The Russians were attacking Army Group North. Southern Poland and East Prussia were threatened, and it was Claus's task to describe the newly formed People's Grenadier Divisions designed to turn that tide. On paper, they were conventional divisions. In fact, they were a lamentation or a laugh.

The house on the Tristanstrasse seemed barer than ever. Berthold was not at home. "I'm tired. I ought to sleep, but probably won't be able to. I'll need steady nerves and a clear head." Reluctantly, he poured a small glass of *Schnapps*. It slid down like molten lava. Then he put out the lights and lay down in bed. The house seemed as restless as himself. The fabric of the floor and walls ticked and stirred. The wind muttered outside, seeming to carry the voices of the dead and gone. He began thinking of the dead he had known, his family dead, some hardly remembered. He recalled the poet, Stefan George, then the war dead. There were a few friends, dead in absentia, and noted only in letters and communiqués. And there were the many he had known only in death, the anonymous dead, whose groans he had heard, whose frozen faces he had seen. How many altogether? He began slowly to count. Presently, as the procession began to merge, he willed himself to cold, quick sleep. No raiders came that night to interrupt his slumbers, and he slept well as though the deed were done.

PART THREE

The Assassin

10

CLAUS LOOKED at his watch. It was 10 A.M. on that twentieth day of July when the plane began to sink toward the cloud floor, through delicate marble sculptures which impeded them not at all. The earth became visible: East Prussia with its splendid lakes and dark, sun-absorbing forests. Farm houses shone in the sun like children's blocks. Here and there were the dilapidated ancestral castles of the Crusaders. In the pastures, horses which had not yet gone to the Russian front still frisked. An airstrip became visible, grew quickly as their own shadow flew to meet them. The plane flashed over some trees, met the speeding grass and bumped down. Brakes were applied. Claus was thrown forward, his briefcase jolting against his leg. The plane slowed. The propeller died and coughed into silence.

A staff car was waiting. Briefly, Claus instructed the pilot to be ready at noon to take off on a moment's notice. Then they began the nine-mile drive to the Wolf's Lair, the cross between a monastery and a concentration camp which was Hitler's headquarters in East Prussia. It was hot. Even the movement of the car did not seem to stir the heavy atmosphere. They all rode in silence, their faces fixed in peaceful expressions. Haeften seemed no longer even to breathe, a wax dummy of a man. "Fear comes in many disguises," Claus thought. "The peacefully smiling one is perhaps the most deadly. I shall have to keep an eye on Haeften."

They arrived at the first checkpoint, which was guarded by the

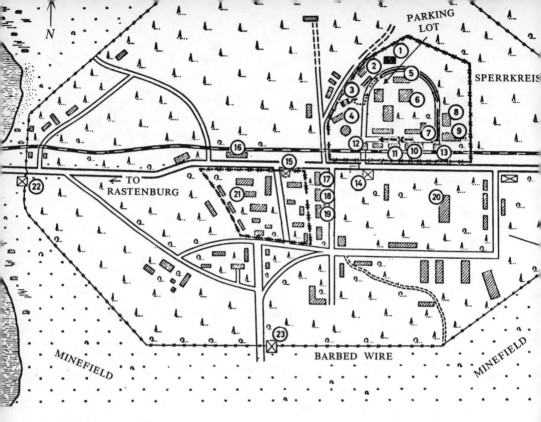

HITLER'S HEADQUARTERS IN RASTENBERG

1. Hitler's bunker
2. Bormann's bunker
3. Conference barracks
4. SS Security Service
5. Tea house
6. Wehrmacht office
7. Keitel's bunker
8. Map room
9. Goering's bunker
10. Jodl's bunker
11. Communications office
   (Fellgiebel)

12. Gate to Sperrkreis I
13. Gate to Sperrkreis I
14. Barrier
15. Inside checkpoint
16. Railroad station
17. Doctor
18. Writing room
19. Post office
20. Speer's bunker
21. Central switchboard
22. Checkpoint West
23. Checkpoint South

SS in their funereal black. Special passes were shown, and they slid through the zebra-striped gate into a belt of minefields and barbed wire. Here the heavily wooded area really began. A thousand yards further on was another checkpoint. News of their arrival was telephoned ahead, and then the car passed into the forest of beech, birch and gloomy pines. It occurred to Claus that a forest of that sort should have been full of birds, rabbits and squirrels, but no life at all appeared. In this wild wood older than memory, no woodsmen left their marks, no witches dwelled in gingerbread houses to lure children. Bits of ground mist hung like dingy cotton in the branches. The heat had begun to shred it away and there was an occasional glimpse of blue sky. Yet the light had a stormy quality and the air bore a chill despite the heat. Claus had a presentiment of evil; like some rolling fog he felt it oozing from this forbidden forest to drown the world. Here and there bunkers and pillboxes squatted in the gloom like cenozoic monsters.

The car was drawn up and parked at the officers' guard post. With a silent salute, Stieff and his aide departed for their quarters. Claus and Haeften walked toward the office of the camp commandant. "Come along now, Haeften." Claus's manner was snappy, intentionally businesslike.

"Well, here we are," said Haeften gloomily, "and I don't like it." His briefcase, containing a spare bomb, seemed too heavy for him. He glanced around apprehensively until his eyes were fixed and held by Sperrkreis I, Hitler's compound. Surrounded by a heavy wire fence seven and a half feet high, patrolled day and night by SS guards, Sperrkreis I included a number of buildings, among them Goering's bunker, Fuehrerbunker I where Hitler lived, and a wooden kennel containing the Alsatian bitch, Blondi. She had arrived as the gift of his secretary, Martin Bormann, and she was intended to cheer Hitler up after the debacle of Stalingrad. No one entered Sperrkreis I without a written pass. If unknown to SS Oberfuehrer Rattenhuber, one had to submit to a physical search for weapons.

As soon as the dog saw them, she began to bark ferociously

from her kennel. All other sounds seemed entrapped by the heavy, humid air. Beams for reconstruction being unloaded by prison workers sounded dully as though they were hitting the bottom of a well, but the dog's alarm cut through the air like a knife.

At the commandant's office they were greeted by Captain von Moellendorff, who escorted them to the "teahouse" for breakfast. Von Moellendorff was a blond, muscular man with a stern face, the replica of a Joseph Thorak statue depicting Aryan virtues at their most dangerous.

Junior officers were already at breakfast when Claus and the others arrived. Late hours were kept here to conform to Hitler's personal schedule, which called for herb tea, nuts and raisins each morning at eleven.

"It's too hot in here to breathe," muttered Haeften, as steaming cups of coffee appeared.

"Champagne might be more refreshing," agreed Claus, trying to lift the mood. *"Ersatz* at that," he added as he drank the coffee. Presently breakfast arrived. "Ah, Captain Moellendorff, what have we here?"

"Sausage, I believe, Colonel Stauffenberg."

"Of what animal, I wonder? Mule, would you say, or horse?"

"I don't know, sir, I'm sure. I should think the Fuehrer would only have pork."

"He doesn't eat meat. Well, whatever it is, it's too much for this knife. Perhaps I ought to try the cereal." He didn't feel like eating now, but he forced himself. The cereal slid down thickly. His stomach registered pain. He tried, but he could not recall how long it had been since he had had any solid food.

Haeften was having trouble. He looked uncomfortable, as though his uniform were full of thistles. Perhaps he was conjuring up images of torn limbs, gouged eyes, spattered blood— the effects of a bomb discharged at close quarters.

"Eat, Haeften. We haven't all day," Claus urged him. "I'm told Il Duce is paying an afternoon visit, which puts us on a rather tight schedule."

Haeften chewed with fatalistic desperation, his ears moving faintly. As though in a nightmare, he tried to consume great quantities of gluey paste without being able to swallow. "What is this stuff?" he asked helplessly.

"I don't know," said Claus. "I've never tasted it before myself, though I may have stepped in it once. I'm sure it's quite nutritious."

Moellendorff broke the spell. He began to laugh. He shook backwards and forwards, and on this cue came satellite laughter. The Colonel was being funny, and so was the Lieutenant. Laughter caught from one to another; jackass laughter, horse laughter, hyena laughter, the laughter of barking seals without rhyme or reason or any end, laughter like the retching of an empty stomach. "This place is mad: they're all hysterical," thought Claus. Haeften looked ghastly. He was trying to remove himself inconspicuously, and the effort was so painful all eyes followed. Laughter wafted him out the door, then stopped abruptly as Claus and Moellendorff rose.

"That's all right, Captain. I'll look after him. I'm afraid my aide tends toward airsickness. It's nothing. Finish your breakfast."

Outside, Haeften leaned against the wall. "I'm sorry," he said abysmally as Claus approached him. "I'll be all right."

"You must get hold of yourself, Haeften."

"I'm not afraid," Haeften protested. "It's this wretched smell."

The heavy atmosphere that surrounded the Wolf's Lair seemed three times exhaled. No wind could stir it, no storm entirely drive it away. Perhaps it was more a matter of the mind, that atmosphere of sweet vegetable spoilage which seemed malignant and foul. Possibly the dark pines exuded some corrosive resin. Claus wondered if, after a week, a month, one would no longer notice. One might leave only to be made ill by other aromas.

Haeften pulled himself up straight. He smiled weakly. "I'm all right now, Colonel. You can count on me."

"Then wait at the car, Haeften. Keep track of your stomach

and that briefcase, and be ready to leave on a moment's notice. Let's part here, and try to smile as you go."

Claus walked alone to the communications building. It stood in damp shade. Toadstools and mushrooms clustered around it like mutilated fingers and toes. In the deepening gloom, they appeared to gain in size, number and distortion. He half expected them to move, to surround the building entirely.

General
Erich Fellgiebel

General Fellgiebel, the chief Army signals officer, was expecting him. Handsome and dignified, he laughed nervously on Claus's arrival, tore off his glasses, rubbed them on his sleeve, and put them back again.

"Everyone is laughing today, General," said Claus. "What a happy place."

They shook hands.

"I see you have your briefcase," said General Fellgiebel.

"Indeed. The whole bag of tricks this time."

Very little needed to be said. While Claus was delivering his briefcase to the map room, Fellgiebel would be prepared to send the signal of success to the Bendlerstrasse offices in Berlin. Then it would be his task to shut down all Rastenburg communications for as long as possible. It was beyond the power of the conspirators to physically destroy the massive signal installation, but the fact that it was in the confused process of being transplanted to a safer rear area might well be in their favor. Otherwise, all Fellgiebel could do was order his operators to pass on no communications. Hopefully, this would put the headquarters out of touch with the world for an hour or two while the coup got underway.

"Good luck then, General," Claus told him.

"And good luck to you." Fellgiebel shook his head slowly like a bulldog which has set its teeth. "Germany, Germany. What will be left of it?"

Claus's next routine stop was at the office of the Army's representative at Hitler's headquarters, General Walter Buhle, to inform him of the Reserve Army situation. General Buhle had been Claus's former superior in the organizational section, but the man's noncommittal voice and impenetrable eyes had prevented Claus from trying to draw him into the conspiracy.

"I'm glad you're here, Colonel Stauffenberg." His tone was condescending, suitable perhaps for a well-trained dog but hardly for a brother officer. Claus stiffened. Then he outlined his report.

"We've allowed only one exemption from combat service," he

said. "It goes to any man over sixty-five who can prove he has a father fighting at the front."

General Buhle stood reflectively. Finally he cleared his throat and rapped his stick against his boot. "I'm glad you've kept your sense of humor, Colonel. However, I recommend that at the staff meeting you keep it locked in your briefcase. Such things just aren't suitable for the Fuehrer. Even a casual remark might be interpreted as defeatist, and upset him. Paint a bright picture, Stauffenberg. Mention the men's eagerness to go, their high spirits. That's my advice. Now," he glared at his watch, "excuse me while I alert General Thadden."

His absence gave Claus a chance to arrange the papers in his briefcase. The bomb lay at the bottom, still dormant, wrapped in a clean shirt. The rubber-shod pliers were in his pocket.

Upon the arrival of Lieutenant General von Thadden, Buhle's Chief of Staff, the three men went together toward Keitel's briefing hut. It was exactly noon when they left Buhle's office.

"How is the good Keitel?" asked Claus as they walked together. He was feeling disembodied, impervious and indestructible. Surely the grim reaper was busy at other chores. "I've heard that, like Napoleon, he's begun to pinch people's ears."

"Give him time," replied General Thadden.

"Gentlemen, some respect," from Buhle. There was little force in his reprimand for, like Keitel, it was his way to move from lap to lap in his progress to the top of the heap in which they were all competitors, and, in the last analysis, enemies.

In the anteroom to Keitel's office, Claus left his cap and belt on the table. There was motive in this beyond simple comfort.

Keitel was in a fussy flap. As maitre d' of Hitler's affairs, the staff meeting, in form at least, was his responsibility. He wished, he said, to conduct it like sweet music for his Fuehrer's ears. "Now we have only fifteen minutes to rehearse, thanks to that Italian." Keitel's tone was petulant. As he spoke, his head wagged as though his florid neck were more fat than muscle, which indeed it was. He's aged, Claus noticed, like the rest of us.

LEFT TO RIGHT: *Goering, Hitler, Keitel, Doenitz*

"Please, gentlemen. If you'll only give me your attention."
They were poring over maps and documents. "Please. Just
the bare essentials today. Your Fuehrer has a very tiring afternoon ahead. You simply can't imagine." Keitel's hands were on
his broad hips. He was up on his toes half the time, Claus
noticed. "And gentlemen," he looked directly at Claus, "nothing depressing. Your Fuehrer must not be troubled. We don't
any of us want to cast a pall over this happy reunion with Il
Duce." Keitel was sniffing loudly but constantly. "Oh, oh, whatever happened to the time? We're simply enslaved here. Gentlemen, would you care to freshen up?" Awkward as a great turtle,
he began to pull on his jacket, which for a moment seemed
a shell too small for his body.

They began to file out.

"Gentlemen, one last thing. No smoking. Remember the Fuehrer has a nose as sensitive as an animal in the forest."

Keitel led the way. He seemed as oblivious to his surroundings, to the trees and sky, as a mole traveling through the soil.

Claus had not gone very many steps from the door when, aloud, he remembered his belt and cap. Keitel stopped, hands on hips. He rose to his toes and settled again. "Very well, Colonel, but please hurry." Claus turned back. "Have some consideration for your Fuehrer!" was hurled after him.

Once inside, Claus asked Lieutenant Colonel John von Freyend, Keitel's aide, if he might briefly use his bedroom to change into a clean shirt. Keitel was already shouting, his voice coming straight from the sinus passages. Claus yawned tremulously and saw himself in a mirror, mouth agape. He opened the case. His hand shook slowly and steadily. There. He'd burrowed down to the bomb and fuse, fumbled for the pliers, brought the two into contact. There was no turning back this time, and yet the glass of the tube seemed too much for him. He couldn't make his fingers close tight enough to break the glass. Then Freyend rapped on the door and, in startled response, his fingers met. The tube had snapped.

"Coming. Coming," he said aloud. Standing before the mirror, he watched a stranger shove the bomb down into the case, cover it with papers and close the latch. He made an effort to flush all emotion from his face, and the mirror image obliged. By the time he had laid his hand upon the door, he was a staff officer again, preparing to deliver a report.

Keitel was waiting with a tortured expression. He offered to carry Claus's briefcase and Claus declined. It was a three minute walk to Hitler's compound, three minutes for the acid to eat. Keitel led the way, as breathless as a rickshaw man in harness. "Hurry, hurry. The Fuehrer will be savage if we keep him waiting."

Claus followed stiffly. His legs seemed wooden. "Damn my legs," he thought.

SS Oberfuehrer Rattenhuber, a big man with a boxer's nose

and the stolid air of a conscientious bully, awaited them. He looked the party up and down with opaque eyes, then directed that the gate be opened.

"What is that in your pocket, Colonel?" he demanded as Claus went by.

"Pocket?" A part of him was terrified, the rest apathetic. He had the weird apprehension that he had been through this exact situation before in some other time or existence. Everything seemed so much clearer, brighter, larger than life. "Oh, yes. My pocket." He pulled out the small pair of pliers. Rattenhuber nodded and passed him on. In its kennel, the dog began to bark and howl, while in Claus's briefcase the bomb whispered in a voice only he could hear: "Ten minutes. Ten minutes."

11

THE CONFERENCE BARRACKS, shelled in concrete, surrounded by gaunt trees, awaited them. Its low dark doorway seemed to squint menacingly as the troop of stiff-faced officers approached. They were self-absorbed, most of them, rehearsing the placating lies they had learned by heart. Claus heard only the bomb beside him, whispering of its terrible life to come, and he moved with sure purpose, the angel of death.

Inside the building it was damp and chill, as though they had entered a cave. The guards were pale men whose eyes were not used to sunlight, who breathed always through ventilators. As they passed the telephone exchange, Claus announced loudly that he expected a Berlin call with information for his report; this so Keitel might hear. All were hurrying down the corridor now, each seemingly anxious to arrive first at the far end, but not wanting that purpose to show.

The conference room was packed. Two dozen of Hitler's "nodding donkeys," as some called them, pressed around an enormous table that filled the room like an elephant in a kitchen. Claus knew some of them, the men he intended to destroy: Jodl, Chief of the Armed Forces Operations Staff; SS group leader Fegelein, representing the Waffen SS; Rear Admiral Voss; General Buhle; Colonel Brandt of the General Staff with Luftwaffe General Korten beside him. Goering, Himmler, Ribbentrop, these three were absent, but Hitler was there. He was surrounded by his toadies, yet completely alone, sealed inside

himself except for occasional volcanic outpourings. He greeted
Keitel as they entered.

"We are having a difficult time today, Keitel," he said, referring to the Russian offensive.

"We shall overcome this reverse as we have all the others,
Mein Fuehrer," Keitel replied, and then he introduced Claus.
"Colonel Count von Stauffenberg, the man who is organizing the
new units."

Hitler nodded. "We have met." Claus returned the greeting
with a salute, wondering if even in sleep the man closed his
terrible, omniscient eyes.

It was 12:35 P.M., five minutes since the bomb had begun to
breathe. Approximately the same time remained until it would
have its say. Lieutenant General Heusinger, chief of the operations branch of the General Staff, whose opening presentation
they had interrupted, continued his report on the situation on
the eastern front. Claus tried to listen and comprehend, but since
he knew he would not be answering any questions, he found it
difficult to concentrate. Instead, he seemed to hear the crumbling
away of metal under the acid's tongue. He had been given a place
at the table next to Colonel Brandt, a man for whom he had great
respect. Brandt was a famous equestrian who had been a winner
at the 1936 Olympic games. Later, he had unwittingly carried
a defective bomb aboard Hitler's plane. At this point in his soon-
to-be-terminated career, he was Lieutenant General Heusinger's
aide.

Claus was about to deposit his briefcase somewhere in the
vicinity of Brandt's feet when Keitel interrupted the speaker who
had been describing the worsening situation east of Lemberg.
"Mein Fuehrer," he said, "perhaps you will hear Colonel Stauffenberg on that point right away?"

Claus froze, but for the one and only time Hitler saved him.
He ordered Heusinger to get the defeatism out of his system, all
of it. As Heusinger droned on, Claus leaned over to Keitel and
whispered, *"Herr Feldmarschall,* I must make an urgent phone
call. The most current figures from Berlin. I'll be back in a min-

ute." His voice was quiet and calm; he hoped not too quiet and calm. Keitel nodded. Thank God he didn't have Fromm to contend with this time.

Then Claus placed his briefcase under the table. He leaned it up against a heavy support as near Hitler as possible. It was almost between Colonel Brandt's legs. That man, whom he scarcely knew but whom he admired as a great horseman, whose life Tresckow had once before imperiled with a bomb, would surely die. Berger, the little gray-faced stenographer, could not possibly survive. He would be killing innocent men. He wanted to draw them out of the room on some pretext, but the stakes were too large for such considerations. At least, if the bomb did its job, it would be a quick and merciful death for those he did not hate but could not save.

"I'll leave my briefcase here," he whispered to Brandt. "I must make a phone call." Brandt looked annoyed but said and did nothing.

It was 12:36 when Claus edged toward the door. Once in the corridor he set out at a brisk pace, a man with an appointment, not a man in flight. At the switchboard, he asked if a call had come for him. Of course it had not. He stepped outside, legs, arms, everything under control except his sweat glands. Even if snow had been flying, he would have been drenched in perspiration. As he passed, the kennel dweller thrust her muzzle up against the wire fence, jaws quivering, ready to protest. She reared up, forelegs pressed wide apart, threw back her head and howled. Blondi, the devil's favorite bitch. She seemed intent on pushing through the iron mesh that restrained her.

Claus saluted the SS guards as he passed out of the compound. They exchanged the greeting without surprise or interest. Officers frequently came and went from the staff meetings. From the gate he walked directly to General Fellgiebel's office. Fellgiebel and Haeften were there, standing before the door. Haeften held the spare briefcase with the extra bomb. He looked very pale.

"Any second now," Claus told them.

They waited. The dog kept up its clamor. Then Lieutenant Colonel Sander arrived. He indicated that their car was ready and reminded Claus that he was expected for lunch by the camp commandant. "Yes, of course. As soon as I've seen Fromm," Claus told him. Sander departed, and the three men were once more alone. How much longer now? A minute? Claus looked at his watch. He held it to his ear. He counted all the way to sixty, then started over again. Something was wrong. He would have to go back to the conference with Haeften's case. The seconds fell away slowly, heavily, like drops of moisture in a limestone cave, much slower than the beating of his heart. The dog's urgent barks continued as the timepiece ticked slowly, silently, without passion or promise.

Claus looked at his watch again. It said exactly 12:43. Too long. "All right, Haeften," he said. "Let's have it." The dog uttered a sharp, rounded howl, a silver whoop of shivering sound, and then the bomb said, "Now! Now!" The explosion was like a call to attention, silencing all questions, silencing the dog, stilling even the private communication of the heart. Pines shivered, debris and a yellow sulphurous cloud rose lazily.

"My God!" Lieutenant Colonel Sander ran out of the communications building. "What was that? What's happening?" He looked overhead for planes.

"Someone let off a round or stepped on a mine somewhere." Fellgiebel passed it off with disinterest.

Claus threw down his cigarette and ground it out with his heel. "Well," he said, "good luck to all of you. Come, Haeften, we must not keep General Fromm waiting." Far away he heard cries of pain. "Let them die quickly," he thought, "but let them die." He could not deny it, the terrible sound was welcome music to his ears. As he walked toward the staff car, he felt younger at every step.

Three checkpoints had to be cleared. The first was within sight of the still rising column of smoke and dust. The sentries of the officers' guard stopped them. Claus leapt out. Finding an officer on duty in the guardroom, he asked if he might use the

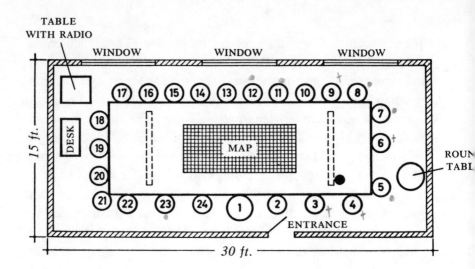

TABLE WITH RADIO

WINDOW　　　WINDOW　　　WINDOW

DESK

18
19
20
21 22 23 24

17 16 15 14 13 12 11 10 9 8

7

6

5

MAP

1 2 3 4

ENTRANCE

ROUND TABLE

15 ft.

30 ft.

BRIEFING IN THE CONFERENCE ROOM, GUEST BARRACKS, AT FUEHRER HEADQUARTERS, 12:30 P.M. ON JULY 20, 1944

●   *Bomb in briefcase under table*

1. *Adolf Hitler.*

2. *General Heusinger, Chief of the Operations Branch of the General Staff of the Army and Deputy of the Chief of the General Staff.*

3. *General Korten, Chief of the General Staff of the Air Force (Luftwaffe); died of his injuries.*

4. *Colonel Brandt, of the General Staff, First General Staff Officer, Heusinger's Deputy; died of his injuries.*

5. *General Bodenschatz, Liaison Officer of the Commander in Chief of the Air Force at Fuehrer Headquarters; severely wounded in the legs.*

6. *General Schmundt, Chief Adjutant of the Armed Forces with the Fuehrer and Chief of the Army Personnel Office; died later of his injuries.*

7. *Lieutenant Colonel Borgman of the General Staff, Adjutant of the Fuehrer; severely injured.*

8. *Rear Admiral von Puttkamer, Naval Adjutant of the Fuehrer; lightly injured.*

9. *Stenographer Berger; killed on the spot.*

10. *Naval Captain Assmann, Admiralty Staff Officer in the Armed Forces Operations Staff.*

11. *General Scherff, Special Commissioner of the Fuehrer for the writing of military history, Armed Forces High Command (OKW); lightly injured.*

12. *General Buhle, Chief of the Army Staff at the Armed Forces High Command (OKW); lightly injured.*

13. *Rear Admiral Voss, Representative of the Commander in Chief of the Navy at Fuehrer Headquarters.*

14. *SS Group Leader Fegelein, Representative of the Waffen SS at Fuehrer Headquarters.*

15. *Colonel von Below of the General Staff, Air Force Adjutant of the Fuehrer.*

16. *SS Hauptsturmfuehrer Guensche, Adjutant of the Fuehrer.*

17. *Stenographer Hagen.*

18. *Lieutenant Colonel von John of the General Staff, Keitel's Adjutant.*

19. *Major Buechs of the General Staff, Jodl's Adjutant.*

20. *Lieutenant Colonel Waizenegger of the General Staff, Keitel's Adjutant.*

21. *Ministerial Counsel von Sonnleithner, Foreign Office Representative at Fuehrer Headquarters.*

22. *General Warlimont, Deputy Chief of the Armed Forces Operations Staff.*

23. *General Jodl, Chief of the Armed Forces Operations Staff; lightly wounded.*

24. *Field Marshal Keitel, Chief of the Armed Forces High Command (OKW).*

phone. The conversation was brief and one-sided. Claus yelled into the receiver at a confounded operator on the other end. "Yes, General, thank you, General," and then banged down the phone with authority. "All right, Herr Lieutenant, we may pass." It was sheer effrontery. The lieutenant twisted his scrawny neck with embarrassment and snapped off a command to the sergeant at the gate. The sergeant swung back the barrier.

Between the first and second checkpoints, the alarm went out. Guards were doubled. This time the staff car pulled up before a *chevaux-de-frise* which had been thrown across the road.

"Open up, Lieutenant. We have permission," Claus demanded.

When no response was forthcoming, Claus approached the barrier on foot.

"Halt!" Claus heard also the crack of a rifle bolt. The rifle was raised and aimed. Behind it was a hard mouth, turned down at the corners, and pale eyes narrowed like cats' pupils in sunlight.

This was known as Checkpoint South. The sergeant who was on duty told him all entry and exit had been forbidden.

"Then put me through to the camp commandant," Claus demanded. He had had a luncheon appointment with the commandant. The conversation might have been awkward had not the commandant's aide, Captain Moellendorff, answered the phone. "This is Colonel Stauffenberg speaking," Claus began. "I'm at the South Gate. You'll recall we breakfasted together this morning? Yes . . . yes . . . Haeften? He's feeling fine now, thank you. Captain, because of the explosion the guard won't let me through the South Gate. I'm in rather a hurry. General Fromm is waiting for me at the air strip. Good. Thank you very much."

As before, he replaced the telephone receiver. "You heard, Sergeant-Major. I'm allowed through."

"I'm sorry, Colonel. In this case I require a direct order." Taking hold of the telephone, he rang up Captain Moellendorff, had his say, and then nodded into the phone. "Yes. Very well. All right, Colonel. You and your party may pass." Without further delay he directed his guards to draw back the *chevaux-de-frise*.

The car lunged forward. One gate remained and then the open road. As they drove up, the two guards appeared to be holding hands. They jumped apart, clicking their heels. The taller one wore steel-rimmed spectacles. His face was pale and homely, the only bright note a garden of pimples flowering upon the tip of his chin. He approached the car. "Colonel Stauffenberg's party?" he inquired. "We have a message concerning you." Claus stiffened. He knew Haeften's hand clenched a pistol. "You're to be allowed to pass without delay." The South Gate, evidently to compensate for harsh treatment, had called through. The last gate swung wide. The car seemed to skim the road on a cushion of air while all about them flowed an endless gust of pure and cleansing oxygen. Liberation! Claus expected its wind to shake the branches of the thinning forest, but when he glanced back, the black mass of trees stood still and stark, hiding its secrets. There was no pursuit, no sound of alarm apart from a long drawn out howl. It went on and on, blending at last with the roar of the car until Claus was sure no dog could maintain such a cry.

Once on the airport road, Claus advised Haeften to get rid of the spare bomb. One after another, the components went out the window. The driver's face in the rear-view mirror became increasingly agitated, but if he was suspicious, his response was not to drive slower, but faster.

Claus urged him on.

There was no sign of special security at the air strip. In fact, it had not been alerted. The plane was waiting.

"Where is General Fromm, Herr Colonel?" the driver asked.

"In the plane, I'm sure. You can stop right here." With the staff car dismissed, they could hardly keep from running to the plane. Neither man looked back, as though the tiger which lurked in their thoughts might be given form by such an act. Logic said no enemy could be hidden on the plane, which had neither radio nor other means of communication, but still Claus's eye swept round for black and crouching uniforms.

The pilot waited alone. "General Stieff not coming?" Claus

shook his head. The pilot shrugged, and sat down to his controls. Haeften slammed the door. The propeller began its slow, choking revolutions. They were away, lifting into a clear and radiant sky. There was no end to visibility. But for the curve of the land, they might have gazed northwest to England across the sea. The plane was fueled to get there, but such a destination had never occurred to Claus. Behind and below them, the blot of Prussian forest shrank and dwindled to an old bloodstain on a yellow carpet. The memory of being pursued by planes in Africa tormented Claus, and he looked back occasionally. There had been other planes on the runway, some armed and faster than their own.

In fact, pursuit would presently be ordered, but it would be based on the conviction that assassins would fly to sanctuary in England. Claus's plane, the HE 111, would be identified and orders sent out to shoot it down, orders which would go to the desk of Major Friedrich Georgi of the air staff. Georgi was General Olbricht's son-in-law, and the order would go no further.

Claus sat back. He took a deep and tremulous breath and closed his eye. It had been an endless day and he felt as though he had just toiled up from damnation. This was a chance to rest on the rim before climbing again.

"Colonel, would you like something? A sandwich?" said Haeften, who was hunched forward in his seat.

"A sandwich? Why, no, thank you, Haeften." He really wanted to be left alone, but Haeften was determined to start a conversation. It was as though he had to go over every detail in order to make it real.

"What was it like, Colonel?"

"You saw the explosion. Like a hundred and fifty millimeter shell."

"Like judgment; a final judgment," Haeften replied. Then, more reflectively, "They must all be dead."

"I'm sorry about Brandt and some of the others. I know your feelings, Haeften. My own are not as different as you probably think."

"As long as he's dead. God knows, perhaps there's no price too high to pay for that."

"Hitler's dead, all right. Thank God for that," replied Claus.

"All the church bells in Germany rang when he was elected. They'll ring all over the world now."

Claus was possessed by a strange happiness. He caught a glimpse of Haeften's face and saw the same emotion, a happiness that overlooked nothing, not even murder. Of course the job was far from finished. They'd disposed of the key figure. His diabolic government remained, but for a few minutes Claus relaxed utterly. Behind closed lids he saw a consoling vision: not banners and glory, simply a glass of warm milk, a lump of soft cheese and some bread. "Haeften, I feel as empty as a barrel with the bottom kicked out. I just might take that sandwich."

By 3:30 P.M. the slow and steady Heinkel was nearing Berlin. Claus pictured the Bendlerstrasse offices a hive of activity. The deed was done. It was too late now to hesitate. They were all of them shackled to whatever happened. Victory or death were the only alternatives. It gave him fervor as well as an odd serenity.

"We have climbed to a summit, Haeften."

"Yes, Colonel, and I like the air."

"Let's hope it will last."

Claus looked below for signs that *Valkyrie* was being implemented. He saw a train moving out of Berlin to escape the dark and the possible air raids. He expected trucks and tanks. "Over there," Haeften pointed. There appeared to be a traffic jam of slow-moving vehicles in columns. He couldn't be sure. With Olbricht and Beck, matters were in good enough hands. Beck was old. He complained of a constant toothache no dentist could locate, but he was a man of great and unswerving conviction. Stuelpnagel, also, was absolutely dependable. Perhaps, with Hitler dead, Fromm had thrown in his lot with them. But in the end it was not the men at the Bendlerstrasse, not Fromm or Beck or himself, who would decide things. As staff officers, they could only issue orders and appeals, by telephone, radio and courier. It was the field generals with loyal troops and heavy weapons under their command who must commit themselves now. If only Rommel had not been cut down. In his place was Kluge. France was the key to it all, and Kluge the key to France. Beck had undoubtedly telephoned Paris by now, and with Stuelpnagel's help they might already have prevailed on Kluge to act. If so, the final issue would be decided before the Heinkel ever set down in Berlin. They had begun to descend. He could feel it in his ears. If they hadn't lost Rommel or if Tresckow had only gotten to the west, there would have been no doubt whatever, but in any case, speculation was vain. He would be back in the center of it all within minutes. Let it be until then. Claus adjusted his seat belt and sat back for the landing.

Ten hours had passed since he had left Berlin. Ten hours, and all that had visibly changed was the position of the sun. Tires shrieked on contact with the runway. The plane bounced forward, struck again and they were safely down.

No SS or Gestapo were waiting for them. There was not even the staff car which Claus had expected. He didn't know whether to be relieved, exasperated or worried. While he sent Haeften to put through a call to the Bendlerstrasse, Claus thanked the pilot. They talked of inconsequential things, of the weather. "It's hot as blood," the pilot said. Then he asked Claus about the prospects for the new planes which had been promised, the jets.

Presently Haeften returned. He'd spoken to Mertz von Quirnheim, Olbricht's aide. A car was on its way.

"He said things were off to a slow start. Some mixup with Fellgiebel."

"They should have gotten things going full steam by now." Claus was indignant.

"I'm not quite sure exactly what's up."

Within a few minutes their staff car appeared. It was nearly 4 P.M. They made good time in light traffic, none of it military. The sidewalks had the look of any other day. "They don't seem to know what's going on," Claus said. Presently they pulled into the Bendlerstrasse and the army building loomed ahead, a massive, dreary tombstone. It was 4:15 when Claus dismissed the driver. No extra guards were posted outside. "What's going on here?" he demanded of the single sentry.

"Why, nothing, sir. It's been a quiet day."

Claus glanced up and down the street. Nothing! He dashed up the steps. Stinging sweat flowed beneath his eye patch. In the entrance hall, the first person he met was Franz Herber, his ex-lieutenant from the Polish campaign.

"Tell me, Herber, has there been any excitement today?"

Herber stared at him and smiled, weary and contemptuous. His reply, when it came, bore a lingering touch of insolence. "Oh, you know, the usual nonsense, Colonel. They don't go along very fast without you." He made it sound as though he were describing the tedious frivolities of a cage full of monkeys at the zoo. "Now you're back, I'm sure the pace will pick up . . . Colonel."

12

A BREEZE BLEW through General Olbricht's office. The windows were open permanently. They had been shattered by the raids, and in the warm weather no effort had been made to replace them. The General was staring out through one of the frames when Claus arrived and touched him lightly on the shoulder. Olbricht spun around.

"Claus! It's you!" He almost stuttered. They grinned weakly at one another like two shipwrecked men who had just had a glimpse of the shore.

"Why is everything so quiet here?" Claus demanded for the third time. "Didn't Fellgiebel call?"

"Well, yes and no. That is, he called, but before he could make any sense, he was cut off. We cried wolf once before. We had to be sure this time before ordering *Valkyrie*."

"My God!" said Claus. "Three hours wasted." There'd been no question this time. The *Valkyrie* orders were to have gone out, regardless of the results of the assassination, and now they were coming back with feeble excuses, just as he had done the time before. "Has nothing whatever been done?"

"As soon as we heard from you at the airport, the *Valkyrie* orders began going out, yes."

"Where's General Beck?"

"He came in a few minutes ago. Hoepner's been here for hours."

Claus tried to appraise the tumbling words, to comprehend

the sense of disorientation which they bore. He tried, too, to assess his friend's resolve. Was it determination he saw in Olbricht's face, or simply a determination to be determined?

"What about Paris? Has . . ."

"That was Beck's job," said Olbricht apologetically.

Claus picked up the desk phone. The lines were clear, and he demanded a lightning call to Stuelpnagel's Paris headquarters in the Hotel Majestic. It was exactly 4:30 P.M. when his cousin, Caesar von Hofacker took the call.

"Ah, Claus. Good. Good. We've been waiting. Stuelpnagel? He's with you, one hundred percent. Yes, I think you can safely say we'll have Paris secured within a matter of hours. Kluge? I don't know, Claus. I can't speak for him. Perhaps if someone at your end . . . Yes, I think Beck would be the one. If Beck would reason with him . . . We can switch you over to La Roche Guyan from here."

"Excellent, cousin," Claus said. "Beck will be calling presently. No, he's not here just now. He's in the building. I'll get back to you."

He had barely hung up when Beck came down the corridor. The old general wore a lounge suit, an odd selection for heading a new government, and he looked dreadful. Under his eyes were dark, liverish crescents. He obviously had been kept from home and its consolations for nights on end. With him was Count Helldorf, head of the Berlin police, whose sardonic eyes seemed to have seen everything and placed faith in none of it.

Olbricht launched a verbal assault upon Helldorf. Why hadn't he subordinated himself and the police force to the Army? Why hadn't he taken steps to secure the streets? Arrest the Gestapo? "Simply because," said Helldorf, "I've heard a rumor that Hitler is not dead."

"That nonsense is supposed to be from Keitel," Olbricht burst out. "If it was Keitel, he's lying. Hitler is dead. Stauffenberg's sure of that much."

"I wouldn't believe he was dead if I read his obituary," countered Helldorf.

"I was there. I saw the explosion," said Claus.

"Ah, but did you see his corpse?"

"Yes, of course!" Claus, too, was shouting now. He wanted to foreclose the argument and the winning of debaters' points; he wanted action.

"One moment," Beck intervened. "We must in all loyalty inform the chief of police that there was a report from Lieutenant General Thiele that Hitler may not be dead. We must decide just . . ."

"That's untrue! That's a damned lie!" Olbricht was near the breaking point.

Claus forced a derisive laugh. "Of course headquarters would deny his death."

"No, no. Please, gentlemen." Beck raised a thin-boned, aristocratic hand. "We're all realists here. We must face the possibilities, whether they are true or not. Helldorf and the rest of us must be prepared for the other side to make claims that the assassination has failed. We must expect similar radio announcements. We must also be prepared for the possibility that the report may be true."

"Listen," said Claus. With an effort, he kept his voice calm. "We're wasting precious time. For me, Hitler is dead, but indisputable proof can't come for hours. If we sit on our hands arguing until the proof comes, we'll all be dead men and Germany will be worse off than it was before. General Beck, I've spoken with Paris. There's some doubt about Kluge's intentions. I think if you would reason with him . . . Tresckow has had some success in the past."

"Of course, Colonel." Beck's face seemed to have composed itself into fresh resolve. He was old, but he had not lost his self-respect. He was tired, but he was not beaten. Firmly he lifted the little black instrument from its cradle.

While Beck was on the phone to France, Claus and Olbricht turned to the problem of General Fromm, who had given them little reason to expect his cooperation. While the two men proceeded to his office, Hoepner changed into his Colonel General's uniform to take over from Fromm, should that be necessary when the course of insurrection became clear.

"General Fromm?" Olbricht began the encounter. "As you know, the Fuehrer is dead. We have brought orders which you must sign, the *Valkyrie* orders, with which you're familiar."

"Hitler dead? That's impossible. Keitel has assured me of just the opposite."

"Field Marshal Keitel is lying as usual," interjected Claus, willing to say anything to put out the last doubts. "I saw Hitler's corpse being brought out."

"So you see, General Fromm," Olbricht continued, "in view of the situation, we have issued the preliminary code word for international disturbance to the commanding generals."

Fromm's face flushed darkly. He shoved his chair back, pounded one fist on his desk. "This is damned disobedience!" he roared. "And what is this 'we,' Olbricht? Who issued the order?"

"My Chief of Staff, Colonel Mertz von Quirnheim."

"Damn it, I'm in command here! Send the Colonel to me. At once!"

When Quirnheim arrived, he confirmed what Claus had already said. Impatient with more profitless debate, Claus sought to end it. "General Fromm, I myself exploded the bomb at Hitler's headquarters. The explosion was like a direct hit with a hundred and fifty millimeter shell. No one survived."

Fromm pointed a finger at Claus as though to give his seething thoughts direction. Should Hitler live and the Nazis prevail, vengeance would be terrible. From the victorious conspirators, the worst he might expect was justice, so Fromm finally made his leap. "Count Stauffenberg, your assassination attempt has failed. You must kill yourself."

"Nonsense. With your cooperation success is assured."

Olbricht intervened again. "General Fromm, now is the time for action. If we fail to strike, our country will be destroyed."

"What does this mean, General?" Fromm persisted in a voice turned shrill. "That you are part of this plot as well?"

"Yes, General, but I'm not one of those that will take control of Germany."

"Then I'm putting the three of you under arrest!" shouted Fromm. "Guards!" No one came except Haeften, who had been standing outside the door.

"Quirnheim, go to the signal center and keep those orders from being sent!" With sheer bluster, Fromm almost had them cowed.

Quirnheim replied as though talking in his sleep. "If I am under arrest, *Herr Generaloberst,* I cannot leave the room." They were playing word games while the fate of a nation hung in the balance.

"You don't realize who's in power, Fromm. Olbricht, let's get this over with," said Claus.

"We must put you under arrest, General Fromm. I'm sorry."

Fromm wasn't about to give in. He surged around the desk, his hands balled into fists. Claus stepped into his path, opposing him with what was left of his one hand. Fromm had gone as far as bluster could carry him. He was not truly a courageous man, and when Haeften thrust the barrel of a small automatic into his belly, his resistance was over.

"You'll all answer for this, before God," Fromm told them. His voice was tremulous now.

"Before God?" Claus replied. "I don't imagine you'll have His ear when the time comes."

"Five minutes, General Fromm," said Olbricht, "in which you must decide."

"And then you'll shoot me."

"We're not like that. It's up to you to choose your side."

"Cowards! If you're to win, you'll have to shoot. You'd better make the streets run red."

In the end, they confined Fromm to his adjutant's room, while Hoepner, uniformed at last, took over Fromm's desk with an apology to his old comrade in arms.

"I'm sorry, too, Hoepner. I'm afraid you're making a mistake." Fromm's tone was oddly compassionate.

The arrests did not end with General Fromm. All SS personnel in the building were taken into custody. Not a shot was fired. Then the situation was explained to the junior army officers. Hoepner spoke first, with a confidence he did not feel. "Gentlemen, the Fuehrer is dead. Field Marshal von Witzleben has taken over supreme command of the *Wehrmacht* and has appointed me here in place of Colonel General Fromm, who has ceased to occupy this office. I am asking you to pursue your tasks as loyally and dependably as you have always done."

As the new head of state, Beck also made a statement. "Germany is at a fateful crossroads. On all fronts, the military situation is hopeless. Each passing day, we endure new defeats and the further destruction of our Fatherland. This can no longer be militarily justified. It is the duty of all who truly love their homeland to do their best to bring this war to a close. Whatever the outcome, we shall at least have done our Christian duty."

There were shouts of jubilation as well as of outrage. A few men went so far as to tear the swastika from the left breast of their tunics. One man cried like a wounded beast. Some were numbed and still. Among this group was Colonel Bodo von der Heyde. He stood with the stiff rigidity of a man who has inadvertently set his foot on the third rail. Smoke might at any moment have been expected to waft from his collar. Then his body relaxed. He went back to his office and his work.

Claus was particularly concerned about Colonel Franz Herber, but Herber was nowhere to be found. Beck and Olbricht were discussing details of general security. "There is one fundamental question," Beck was saying. "Will the sentries shoot if necessary?"

Olbricht's hands rose and fell in a limp gesture. There was no way of knowing. "Then," continued Beck, "I recommend you gentlemen arm yourselves." Olbricht had a pistol ready. Beck offered a spare to Claus, who declined. "My hand isn't much good, General. Besides, Haeften is already armed. He'll look after me."

With the preliminary orders on their way, Fromm under

arrest, and the Bendlerstrasse headquarters secured, the conspirators were fully committed. They were well beyond the point of no return, yet they had virtually no troops under their direct command. However, they possessed one powerful weapon, and one only—the telephone. While Beck tried once again to reach Kluge in France, Claus continued to exhort the district commanders in Germany. He spoke with authority into the cold black ear. Most of the officers he spoke to expressed loyalty to the new government in distant, metallic voices. But what happened when the connection was broken? He wanted at least to see their faces, to hear his urgings transformed into commands. The desperate need was not for well-wishers, but for tanks and planes and armies on the march.

In the corridors, the bustle increased. Everyone seemed to be sliding about on casters. Phones rang incessantly. Supplementary orders were going out over the teleprinter at such a rate that the signal traffic officer found all his own circuits blocked, and the man's eagerness to do his job well led to the commission of a fatal error. Claus had already impressed him with the need for speed and so, without confirmation, he began to direct the signal overflow through *Oberkommando der Wehrmacht* circuits. These lines were all channeled through Hitler's headquarters in East Prussia.

There a startled operator relayed the messages to his commander. For the first time the bomb, which at first had been thought to fall from the sky and only later had been attributed to a mutilated colonel, was finally associated with a larger plot. Keitel immediately ordered all such messages held, substituting for them a report that Hitler lived and that a military plot was afoot to overthrow the government. Conflicting reports began to go back and forth, ripples shattering the clear image of conspiracy. Presently only "Fuehrer priority orders" were being carried by the *Oberkommando* circuits.

Claus was unaware of this blunder. He had problems of his own. Field Marshal Witzleben was missing, temporarily lost to the conspiracy of which he was the military figurehead. Also, the Guards Battalion from Doeberitz, which was to be the conspiracy's sword in Berlin, had not arrived. Instead, unexpected and uninvited, came SS Colonel Piffraeder, whose principal claim to fame had been the task of exhuming and destroying Jewish corpses before the Russian advance. With him were two SS bullies. The three clicked their heels like pistol shots and delivered the Hitler salute.

"Where is Colonel Stauffenberg?" Piffraeder demanded.

"Speaking. Won't you come in? Well, you are in, aren't you? May I help you?"

"I have an order calling for your arrest," replied Piffraeder, upon whom it must have slowly been dawning that all was not as usual in the Bendlerstrasse. As he spoke, he toyed nervously with the hilt of the black dagger which hung from his belt. He seemed to smile, but it was only a tension about the lips.

"Colonel," said Claus, "your zeal is commendable. Kleist, see that these men are made comfortable." Unresisting, the SS trio joined Fromm. Within fifteen minutes he had a fourth companion, General von Kortzfleisch, district commander for Berlin. Even when Claus told him that Witzleben was absent, the General would speak to no one else, and doggedly insisted that he would stay loyal to his Hitler oath.

"How can you talk of oaths when Hitler has broken his to the people a hundred times?" Claus asked him. But Kortzfleisch had nothing more to say, and he joined the other prisoners.

Meanwhile, orders had gone out for the takeover of all signal installations and broadcasting stations, and for the arrest of all senior Nazi officials, concentration camp guards, and resisting Waffen SS commanders. This produced a flood of denials, doubts and refutations which drove Claus back to the telephone. Here he steadfastly denied all rumors, exhorting everyone to carry out the orders of the new high command.

It was half-past six when he recognized Colonel Hassell's voice on the other end of the line. "Ah, Hassell. What is it?"

"Stauffenberg, a call has come through from Fellgiebel at the Fuehrer's headquarters."

"Yes, yes. Go ahead. What did he say?"

"Stauffenberg, I feel I should repeat his message word for word. He said, 'What are you people up to? Are you all insane? Hitler is now in the tea room with Mussolini. Presently there will be a radio message.' That's all he said, nothing more."

"That doesn't sound like Fellgiebel," Claus insisted, and yet the specter hung in the air. He banished it with an effort. "Someone's impersonating him." But lie or no lie, a radio message followed within twenty minutes over the *Deutschlandsender:* "A bomb attack was made upon the Fuehrer today. The following of his entourage were severely wounded as a result: Lieutenant General Schmundt, Colonel Brandt and Herr Berger of his staff. The following were slightly injured: Colonel General Jodl, Generals Korten, Buhle, Bodenschatz, Heusinger, Scherff, and Admirals Voss, von Puttkammer, also Captain Assmann and Lieutenant Colonel Borgmann. The Fuehrer was unhurt apart from minor burns and contusions. He continued with his work immediately and, as intended, received the Duce for a long conversation. Shortly after the assault, the *Reichsmarschall* called on the Fuehrer."

"Lies!" Claus struck the desk as he stood up. The wolf he knew to be dead in his lair. Still there was an instant of doubt, brief but insistent as a streak of lightning across a black sky, and undeniable was the failure to seize the radio station. Possession of the *Deutschlandsender* had been given first priority. What had gone wrong? All Olbricht could say was that, to the best of his knowledge, a squad had gone out to take and hold the station. Claus was left with the unhappy choice of trying to fix the blame or of framing a denial. "The communiqué given out over the wireless is incorrect," he wrote. "The Fuehrer is dead. The measures already ordered are to be carried out with maximum speed." He sent the command off without hesitation. He was chilled but also strengthened by the knowledge that their course was inexorably set. Even the specter of Hitler alive, his bomb ravaged body held together by some unnatural effort of the will, could only urge on their efforts now.

The electric clock on the wall announced the hour of 7 P.M. with a snapping of springs. The small hammer fell back to await another hour. With rushing dark clouds evening was descending over Berlin, over the rubble and over the dead. Allied bombing planes would come with the night, seeking out Nazi and conspirator alike with indifferent malice.

Presently Field Marshal Witzleben arrived from his estate in Zossen, a baton thrust under his right arm. Officers stood to attention as he passed. His face was purple with fury and his neck as red and wattled as a turkey gobbler's. He strode down the corridor, muttering to himself, and entered Claus's office. "My God, Colonel Stauffenberg, what's going on here? Why haven't you been able to shut up that little club-footed stallion?" He was referring to Goebbels. "Why haven't we control of that radio station? And where's the support? Where's this army I'm supposed to command?" Six hours late himself, but he wheeled about like a battleship to deliver a final broadside. "Stauffenberg, you've made a fine mess of things!"

"Tanks are on their way, Field Marshal," Claus told him calmly. "They'll be here any minute."

"And the radio station? We have to be prepared to take lives, Stauffenberg."

At this point, General Beck entered. Witzleben saluted his supreme commander with his baton. It was the only pause in his tirade. "Gentlemen, this is a fine mess."

"Of course," said Beck. "The situation is critical. How could it be otherwise?"

"Critical! It's hopeless. I advise you people to flee for your lives. If I had realized the state of affairs, I would have avoided Berlin like the plague."

"There's a risk in every coup d'état," replied Beck.

"Yes, but it should have a ninety percent probability of success."

"Nonsense." Hoepner was in the argument now. "Fifty-one percent is sufficient."

"Eighty percent. I'll say no less than that."

"How could you expect to get eighty?"

It was a farce, if farce can be said to blend with tragedy.

"Gentlemen, please stop shouting." Beck's voice, as usual, was calm and controlled.

"I'm not shouting, damn it!" thundered Witzleben.

"Please, Field Marshal. Sit down and relax. Be a good soldier," Claus urged.

But they remained on their feet, all of them taking deep breaths as though they had just competed in a cross-country race.

Beck tried to soothe them. "Witzleben, you may be right in all you say, but it's too late for such arguments. It's too late to look back. For you, too. Orders signed with your signature have gone out."

"Damn it, why wasn't I consulted?" Witzleben delivered this line like a grenade. "I'm not making a fool of myself in this mess, no thank you. No, you don't need me." Without further comment, he left the room and marched down the corridor to drive away in his Mercedes back to his country seat fifty miles from the city. It was not far enough.

Throughout the next hour the phone rang constantly. Munich reported that the orders from the Bendlerstrasse were being carried out. Nazis were being systematically arrested. General Freiherr von Esebeck, the commanding general in Vienna, called in and asked to speak personally with Fromm. Claus intercepted the call and persuaded Esebeck to begin arresting senior Nazi officials. In Koenigsberg, the district which contained Hitler's headquarters, Claus had no luck, but otherwise reports from the provinces were encouraging. Frankfurt, Hamburg, Stettin and Prague all called in acknowledging the new authorities.

Claus took telephone calls in his own and in Fromm's adjoining office. Darkness was settling over the city now and with it came the darker question. Did Hitler live? More and more often Claus heard himself repeating, "Keitel is lying. Don't believe Keitel. Hitler is dead. Here everything is going full blast." Depending on the voice at the other end of the telephone line, his own voice was sometimes friendly and persuasive, sometimes stern and commanding, sometimes imploring. "You must stand fast. Make sure your chief doesn't back down, Mayessen. I'm relying on you. Don't disappoint us." And on the other phone, "Yes, he's definitely dead. Absolutely no question," repeating and repeating the words as automatically as a robot. He talked on with the weary intensity of one who repeats for the hundredth time a strong conviction which is constantly being misinter-

General
Guenther von Kluge

preted. "Dead . . . yes. Hitler is no longer alive." Two small fists seemed to press from behind, trying to shove through his eye sockets. "I mustn't tire," he told himself. "I must keep on."

The next news was good. The Guards Battalion, under a Major Remer, had finally arrived. It was cordoning off the government quarter, and had met with no opposition. Again the scales had swung into equilibrium. The deciding weight seemed elsewhere. In France, perhaps. Claus had kept in regular touch with Army headquarters in Paris, where the SS officers were now under arrest. But it was Kluge and his fighting men they needed, and Kluge was still out of touch when Beck entered Claus's office. "They're expecting Kluge back any minute," said General Beck. "I told them to put the call through here . . . if it comes." He sat down heavily. "It will be a trial of strength." He filled a glass with water and held it to his lips, gulped half and wiped his chin. "I'm an old man," he said. "I'm older than I thought."

Claus looked at him, smiling. "You're an old fox, General. You don't worry me. No, you've the measure of Kluge any time."

Just then the phone rang. Claus answered it. "It's for you," he said, handing the receiver to Beck. Beck's hand tightened on the telephone with a fierce grip as though he clutched a life preserver. "Yes, yes," he said. Then, turning a weary face toward Claus, he forced a smile. "I have him. I have Kluge on the line."

13

"*WHAT DO YOU MEAN*, you can't think?" Beck spoke into the receiver as though it were a megaphone. "Kluge, there's nothing to think about. You're either with the Army or with the Nazis. It's as simple as that. Kluge, I now ask you clearly. Do you approve of our action and will you put yourself under my orders? Speak up . . . I can't hear you." Beck sat listening, nodding, the lines in his face beginning to tighten. "Damn it, Kluge, that's no answer." Again he was silent, holding the telephone as though he heard private music. He put the instrument down as if it were heavy and very brittle. His head sagged forward. When he looked up, the result of the conversation was written in the deeper crease between his eyes, in the folds beside his nose, in the turn-down corners of his mouth. "That's so like Kluge. He just hung up. Not even the courage to say no. He's 'conferring with his staff.' His staff . . . I've always suspected he kept it in a bottle."

General Beck tried to rise, winced, and sat down again. "It's up to you now, Colonel Stauffenberg." His voice was once more low and husky. "I don't know what more can be done. I'm too old for this. I'm sick to death for peace and quiet. Do you understand?" He spoke to Stauffenberg, who might have been his son, as though Claus were the older and wiser of the two.

"Of course, General."

Beck rose then. The two men saluted one another and Beck turned to go. Claus wiped his eye with the back of his hand.

Outside in the corridor the clamor seemed to have slackened. Claus had a feeling the whole conspiracy was melting away, losing direction. He knew what had to be done, or at least all that he could do. His lonely and frustrating role was to keep on the telephone, encourage the district commanders, deny the rumors, mobilize troops whenever possible. "No, the *Wehrmacht* has taken over full state powers. Yes, the Home Army has the authority to give orders. You understand? Yes, of course the Reich is endangered. As is customary in times of peril, its army is assuming control. Listen, it's very possible you'll be issued counter-orders. You have already? Then disregard them! Yes, disregard anything that doesn't come through Witzleben and this office."

Some listened, and some obeyed. Many good men wavered, haunted by Hitler's ghost, whether dead or alive. Sometimes, before Claus had finished speaking, he would hear a joggle of the switch and the line humming dead in his ear. "Hello? Hello?" Sometimes he would receive furious indictments and accusations of treason. Then he would clutch the receiver until his nails turned white. Occasionally he banged down the phone to give some Nazi devil's eardrum a shock.

The element of surprise had been too long withheld while Claus was en route to Berlin. Now it had clearly run its course. The enemy was gathering itself. Before nine o'clock came the order from Hitler's headquarters at Rastenburg that henceforth, SS Reichsfuehrer Himmler was to supplant General Fromm as Commander in Chief of the Reserve Army. That did no harm. Fromm was no use to them anyway, and Himmler was not loved, even among those Army chiefs who wavered in their loyalties. A radio announcement at 9 P.M. was far more damaging. Claus did not hear it directly but was told of it by Olbricht. "What now?" Claus asked in a voice hoarse from telephoning. The look in his fellow conspirator's face told him their plan had met with unalterable and terrible reverse.

"He lives," Olbricht whispered. "Hitler lives."

The statement ripped through the coherent flow of ideas.

Like the invulnerable monster in some horror film, Hitler, blood-smeared and shattered but still terribly alive, seemed to be slouching toward them. "He's going to speak later on the radio," Olbricht was saying.

Deep down, Claus accepted this, somewhere in that region of the brain which controls the primitive functions beneath consciousness. But his own physical survival was involved in the truth of the statement. As long as the flash and fury of the bomb burned behind his eye, he would deny it. "Why doesn't he speak now, if he's alive and able? Why not now?" Claus made a lie of it. "Surely they're stalling for time, trying to undermine our confidence. You can see that."

"Perhaps," Olbricht replied, but conviction had gone out of him.

"Have you seen Beck?"

"Sitting in my office. He looks ill."

"No word from Kluge?"

"None."

But if one moment pulled down their hopes, the next raised them up again. Colonel Mueller, deputy commander of the infantry school at Doeberitz, reported in, asking for a written order giving him command of the school. Full of enthusiasm, he spoke of taking his men to capture the broadcasting station, of guarding the Bendlerstrasse.

"They're just boys, aren't they?" Claus asked him.

"The best sort of soldiers," Mueller insisted.

"We can use any sort," Claus admitted, "and quickly."

The need for military strength was soon emphasized by the inexplicable withdrawal of the Guards Battalion. One minute it was there in the street outside and the next it was gone. Why, and under whose orders? The effect was sinister, and it left the Bendlerstrasse almost unprotected. At 10 P.M. General Olbricht assembled the junior officers. "Gentlemen," he said, "we have been watching developments with increasing concern. Catastrophe looms on the horizon. Steps must be taken to forestall it. We depend on your support." To those not otherwise employed,

*General
Karl Heinrich
von Stuelpnagel*

he assigned the task of guarding approaches to the Bendlerstrasse, but he met with some verbal opposition.

"Why do we need guards here if everything is in order? I think
we deserve more of an explanation." This came from Herber,
who had kept in the background until now. There were three or
four others who stood with him in dissent. Major Fliessbach and
Lieutenant Colonel von der Heyde were among them.

"I'm appealing to you, not giving an order," Olbricht informed
them. Herber wanted more factual information, but Olbricht

would not give it. He dismissed them. "Go home, Herber, and take your comrades with you. This isn't a debating society."

Meanwhile, Claus stayed by his telephone. It rang more in his head than in reality, a terrible, incessant death knell which continued to ring even when he tried to listen to a communication from the other end of the line. Beyond that ringing, silence was growing in the building. I must try Kluge one more time, he thought, and ordered the lightning call. It went through quickly. The voice at the other end spoke through crackling static. "You are Stauffenberg, aren't you?"

"Yes, that's correct. Is this . . ." and then the line went dead.

His head began to feel very large, very empty and echoing. His thoughts ran in circles, grasping at things that were beyond the possibility of being changed. "He lives." The two words seemed branded across the sky. Even if Hitler lay in fragments, torn beyond recognition, he lived still in the fears and doubts and hopes of too many Germans. He stalked the streets of Berlin, moved the hands and tongues of field commanders. Living or dead, he had won again.

"Hello? Hello, we've been cut off. . . . Hello." There was not even an operator at the other end. He joggled the switch. "Hello?" Claus began to feel strangely resigned, with a drowsy sense of unreality. His consciousness seemed to shrink toward a secret place deep within himself where he would be safe, where he could rest. Just for a moment he relaxed with his head on the desk, then he forced himself upright. Once more he grasped the telephone. Outside in the corridor he heard a growing clamor of voices as though men were fighting there.

He would try Kluge once again. This time he got an operator, but the call which finally went through was not to the field headquarters in France, but to Stuelpnagel's Paris office. Stuelpnagel's chief of staff, Colonel Linstow, answered. "It's all over here," Claus admitted, and could hardly believe his own voice was speaking such words. "You're on your own. You must take what action you deem fit." Out in the corridor, voices were louder. A shot was fired. Perhaps Linstow heard it over the phone, for he said, "Colonel, are you there? Is there any chance for you to escape?"

Escape? Claus had never considered the possibility. In his mind's eye he pictured the back stairway, the subway entrance, humiliating abandonment and eventual capture. A man with one hand and one eye would not be inconspicuous. In fact, Major Georgi, Olbricht's son-in-law, had an arrangement for the conspirators to escape abroad in a Luftwaffe target-towing plane, but no one had taken the idea seriously.

"We'll stand fast here," he said into the phone, and only then realized he spoke into the buzz of a broken connection. For some time he sat where he was. The ground seemed to have evaporated underfoot, and he had the breathless sensation of falling. You don't fall this far and survive, he thought.

A moment later Lieutenant Haeften backed into the room. He held a pistol in his right hand.

"Are we being overrun?" Claus asked him.

"Yes, sir. I'm afraid we are."

"So we've failed again," Claus said. He felt calmer than he had in months. This failure was final. There was peace in such absolute certainty.

"Haeften, if need be, will you use that gun?"

His aide looked at the weapon as though he held something alien and corrupt. "They're too well armed. It would be useless." He strode to the window and looked down, perhaps considering a jump.

"Not on them, Haeften. On me." Haeften turned, horror in his face. "You might help clear yourself that way."

"I couldn't. No, I can't kill anyone." That had been their trouble from the start. They'd had no appetite for blood. "I'll do anything else."

"Make your will, Haeften. Make your will."

The din mounted in the corridor. Staccato words volleyed from the walls. "For or against the Fuehrer? You . . . you . . . what about you?" They were nearing Claus's office when he stepped out to meet them: Herber, Heyde and some others, all

armed with pistols and submachine guns. "Treason!" shouted
Heyde as he raised his pistol and fired. Claus spun backwards,
shot in the left arm. He dove for Fromm's office and slammed
the door behind him. The other principles were quickly rounded
up: Olbricht, Haeften, Beck. All were forced at gunpoint into
Fromm's office where Claus stood helpless, his only functional
arm numb and dripping blood. Had there been a gun in his
pocket, he could not have killed himself now.

Herber, his tongue lying upon his lower lip in a caricature
of a smile, surveyed the conspirators. "We understand something against the Fuehrer is going on. My comrades and I remain faithful to our oath. We demand to see General Fromm."

"Of course. That can be arranged," said Haeften. Herber
and the others did not yet know that Haeften was a conspirator.
Haeften and two of the rebels went out. General Hoepner, at
gunpoint, took their place. He looked like a weary old crane
who'd stood out in a storm, his arms hanging like limp wings.

Fromm had been transferred one floor down to his private
quarters, and presently they heard him coming, his boots
crunching in the corridor. Fromm always marched like the
front legs of a bulldog. Not expecting this sudden turnabout,
he'd downed a bottle of wine which his guards had given him.
His face was incandescent rose, his eyes as blue as lakes fed
by spring snow.

"Now, gentlemen, the reckoning."

In a spasm of effort, Haeften declared himself, his gun raised
to shoot the general down. But Claus jarred against him. "No,
Haeften. Don't." There was no use in petty vengeance now.
Without resistance, Haeften surrendered his weapon.

"I do not intend to treat you as you treated me this morning," Fromm told them. "Surrender your arms."

Beck alone still had a pistol. "You won't make your old
commanding officer do that, Fromm," he said quietly. "I will
keep my weapon for personal reasons. You cannot deny me
this one privilege."

"Keep it, so long as it points toward yourself."

"At this moment I am thinking of the old days," Beck said.

"Get along with your job now," Fromm told him.

Beck faltered. He shoved his shoulders forward like the doors of an empty cupboard he could not close. The pistol wavered against his forehead. The shot, when it came, splashed a crimson whiplash across his brow. Grazed only, the general fell back against his chair.

"Did it fire?" he asked, bewildered.

"Help the old man," Fromm told his aides. Two officers, Herber and Heyde, stepped forward. "Take his gun."

"No, no," Beck insisted. "I'm an officer. I shall find my own way out of this unhappy situation."

Fromm shook his head. "Poor old man, he hasn't the strength." He turned to the other prisoners, Haeften, Merz von Quirnheim, Olbricht and Stauffenberg. "And you, gentlemen. Have you any last requests? Something you wish to record on paper? You have a few minutes."

Olbricht and Hoepner both wanted to write to their wives. Claus could not have written a word had he wanted to, and he did not dare think of Nina and the children for fear he would break down.

Fromm went out into the corridor where he could be seen conferring with other officers. Beck sat stunned; his weapon had been taken away. There was the sibilant sound of pens on paper. Claus waited so calmly through it all that those around him must have thought he was not human or that he did not know what was happening.

After five minutes, Fromm returned. "Gentlemen, I hope you have finished. Please be quick in consideration of the others." Then his manner became more formal. "In the name of the Fuehrer, I have convened a court-martial. Four men have been found guilty of treason and are condemned to death: General of Infantry Olbricht, Colonel of the General Staff Merz von Quirnheim, this colonel whose name I have forgotten and this lieutenant," referring to Stauffenberg and Haeften. Then he addressed Herber. "You will see to the necessary arrangements in the courtyard."

"My pleasure, General." Herber looked at Claus with a half triumphant smile.

"General Beck, can you hear me? General?" Fromm's voice was loud, but oddly solicitous.

Beck looked up. His eyes were dead already. "May I have another pistol?" he asked. "If it doesn't work this time, then please help me."

"All right. Try again. Use mine." Fromm snapped a cartridge into the chamber and Beck did as he was told, grazing himself for a second time. He slumped forward, blood seeping down his face. Claus watched the grim performance as though witnessing a dream. Loss of his own blood was making it seem the more unreal, a fantasy played out by stolid actors.

"Help the old fellow," Fromm said. Heyde stepped up, aimed at the back of the General's neck. He fired, and the horrid drama was over.

The last tremor of life had scarcely left the old General's body when the other four prisoners were ordered down the stairs.

"Can you make it?" Haeften asked.

"I'm not sure," Claus replied. His sleeve was a red flag.

"Lean on me, then."

They went on together.

"Tell me, Haeften. You have not lost your courage?"

"I hope not, Colonel," but he was paler than the ghost he expected soon to be.

"We must be good soldiers for a little while," Claus told him, mouthing words of comfort fit for a child who'd cut his knee. "It has not all been a waste, believe me. You won't be dying for nothing."

"You would do it again, wouldn't you, sir?"

"Yes, again and again, no matter what the consequences."

Claus's throat was dry and his stomach empty, but that was all right. It would soon be over; the weariness, the fear. He had tried, God knows. What else could he have done? Now he need only make a decent end. "A few minutes and I won't be." That was a peaceful thought. Death held no fears for him. He did not dread the process. He knew pain and he was not really afraid of what might follow. After Nazi Germany, Hell could furnish few surprises. But he was afraid of the loss of light and love, of not seeing Nina again, and the children. What had he done to them? There was the real pain, the cutting guilt. He must not think of them or he would make a bad end. Even so, if the coup had only succeeded, if the bomb had done its job, if Kluge had risen from all fours . . . so many "if's" . . . then death would be a fair price to pay. For many of them, the sun had gone down for the last time. It was black night all over Germany. The dawn would not come again for him; perhaps not for his children, perhaps never for Germany. Yet there were men still alive, those who might survive what was to come, with hands ready to carry forward what he had tried to do and bring their native land into a new day. This was his only consolation at the last.

The procession of prisoners debouched into the stone-flanked quadrangle of the Bendlerstrasse. The hooded headlamps of an armored car lit the scene like a stage set. Tall, sharply sculpted shadows mingled on the walls, and the wail of the night's first air raid gave orchestration. Swaggering, satisfaction in every joint, Herber intercepted them at the entrance. This was his victory, his vintage revenge. "To the south wall, if you please," he directed them. "We don't want to break any windows." He walked closer to Claus. "Well, Colonel Stauffenberg, any last messages?"

"Yes, Herber. I have one for you. Watch closely. We will show you how it is done. You'll need to know, Herber. Soon." Herber took a step back. His face could have been no more stricken had he glimpsed the Gorgon.

Heinz Ludwig Bartram, Fromm's adjutant, who had lost his leg at the front, performed the last ritual. There was no offer of cigarettes, no request for blindfolds, but there were white target patches for the firing squad. Hitler's army never lacked for volunteers to man such a squad, but in the present haste only a platoon of fireworkers was available. They were more talented at directing a stream of water than at aiming a gun. So Bartram pinned white paper circles to each prisoner's breast in order to help their aim. When he came to Claus, the pin accidentally found flesh. "I'm sorry," Bartram said. He seemed genuinely disturbed. "Did I hurt you?"

"Soon you will make me laugh," Claus told him. "Everyone's tired. Everyone wants to go home. Let's get this finished."

Overhead, the Perseids flung themselves through endless space so that creatures on earth might count that interstellar hail and make their wishes. Wish that they would love one another forever. Wish that the Russians would not come with their vengeance. Wish that the bombers would let their iron death fall elsewhere. Tomorrow would be a fine summer day, thought Claus, a good one for taking the children over the mountain as he had so often promised. He did not wish for that, however. He could wish only that the firing squad would aim true the first time. They stood but a yard and a half from him. Two steps forward and he would press against those guns. He wanted to pray, but the words of the Lord's Prayer evaded his memory. He knew only the beating of his heart, the blood still oozing down his arm. He must hold himself straight and stare into the darkness between the headlights. A command was being given. The rifles were aimed. "Long live free Germany!" he shouted with anger, reproof and overwhelming regret. Then the flash of the volley burned on his retina and he fell with his friends.

AFTERWARDS

AFTER CLAUS VON STAUFFENBERG'S hasty withdrawal from the conference room at Rastenburg, East Prussia, Colonel Brandt had found that the briefcase left in his charge made it difficult for him to lean toward the map which Heusinger was using to illustrate his report. Consequently, he had moved it to the other side of the table's stout support, a momentary convenience which rewrote the list of those who were to die and altered fate entirely. During the bomb's final minutes of inertia, four inches of solid oak separated Hitler from its impending blast.

As the last strand of copper wire was eaten away, Lieutenant Colonel Heusinger was describing the situation in Army Group North, giving catastrophe a clinical distance. "The Russians are moving a considerable force northwards, west of the Duna. Their leading troops are already southwest of Dunaburg. If the Army Group does not withdraw from Lake Peipus, a disaster will—" Then the bomb flashed and roared. The table rose in fragments, the ceiling fell, the windows burst outwards. The injured cried out for help. The unhurt staggered about, coughing in the smoke. Adolf Hitler beat at the top of his head, which was wreathed in flames. But it was Keitel, moaning with compassion, who extinguished the blaze with his own soft hands, then threw his arms about the man he worshipped.

"Mein Fuehrer, you're alive! You're alive!"

He dragged Hitler, half-walking, half-staggering, out of the smoke. This was the scene witnessed by Fellgiebel after Stauffenberg's departure, and it was the basis for his confused message.

At first, Hitler insisted a plane had dropped a bomb; one of the British Mosquitoes with their wooden construction which always got through the radar defenses. Jodl, who was cut about the head, blamed the foreign construction workers. Not for an hour was Stauffenberg's rapid departure remarked upon. By then, Himmler had arrived from his headquarters on Lake Maursee; Himmler, the ex-school teacher, who liked to smack boys' wrists with a wooden ruler; Himmler, whose long wrinkled neck was never red with agitation. He took over the investigation, and at once singled out Stauffenberg as the assassin. He telephoned Piffraeder in Berlin to arrest the fugitive should he appear. Then he pronounced, "Mein Fuehrer, you can leave it all to me," and himself departed for the capital.

After the blast: wreckage of the conference room at Fuehrer headquarters

Meanwhile, the other members of Hitler's court were hurrying to Rastenburg. Goering, Doenitz and Ribbentrop came from their nearby headquarters to marvel at Hitler's escape, to defend their own loyalty, and to shift suspicion from themselves. They arrived in time for a last mad tea party given by Hitler for Benito Mussolini. Il Duce was over sixty now, and he had already been deposed as the fascist dictator of Italy. His round thyroidal eyes were set in slack gray skin. Obviously, he had passed beyond political ambition. He had come from Italy by train, seeking a savior. With him was Marshal Graziani. When they arrived at the Rastenburg station, the air was misty and damp with approaching rain. The dark pines stood as silent sentinels in the heat, but for Mussolini, the sun shone. Hitler awaited him on the station platform. The Fuehrer, the only leader now, was wrapped in a heavy cloak despite the heat. His face was white, his right arm in a sling. Cotton wool bloomed from his damaged ear.

The two embraced with real warmth, survivors in the eye of a hurricane. "Duce, I sympathize with your problems. An infernal machine has just now been set off. At me! Look! Trousers ruined, hair scorched. My buttocks are like the backside of a baboon. I can tell you how it feels to be tattooed. But I survived. That's the important thing. A miracle." With this Hitler, hitching up his right shoulder as he went, led his old comrade to the car which would take them to the Wolf's Lair and an inspection tour of the damage. "Frankly, Duce, I regard this event as the pronouncement of Divine Providence." Mussolini's eyes were two raw and wobbling eggs as he listened. He viewed the splintered conference room with consternation while Hitler demonstrated just how he had been leaning over the table, his weight on his right and now bandaged arm.

Mussolini's ears, which had long been attuned for the twang of an assassin's bullet, were pricked for the ticking of a bomb. He was full of gloomy apprehension, but he managed, "A marvelous escape. Truly marvelous."

"Marvelous? It's more than that. It's God's intervention. Look at this room, at my uniform. When I reflect on this, I know

Hitler greets Mussolini at Rastenburg

nothing will happen to me. Clearly it is my divine task to continue on and bring my great enterprise to completion. This isn't the first time I've escaped death providentially. You'll recall in Munich when I was making a speech, and then suddenly I left just before a bomb went off. That wasn't accidental, Duce. It was a voice. I heard an inner voice saying, 'Get out! Get out!' and I obeyed it. What has happened here is simply a confirmation. I am now more than ever persuaded that the objectives for which I've struggled so long will survive the present hazards and all will come to a good end." His voice rose prophetically.

"You are correct, Mein Fuehrer," exclaimed Mussolini, allowing himself to be persuaded. "God has put His protecting hand upon your shoulder."

At 5 P.M. these two met with the other guests in the tea house, the only structure in Rastenburg which even on a rainy evening retained a certain lightness and gaiety. Alice and the Mad Hatter might comfortably have sat there over their cups to discuss politics in a world equally deranged. Keitel and his staff had lavished particular care upon this affair, a ritual of innocent pleasure which even men of destiny could enjoy together.

"It's only a snack, gentlemen," Keitel apologized. "I hope it's satisfactory." The table was set with a silver tea service, the pots full of healthy herbs; peppermint, camomile and linden. The trays were spread with *petits fours* and little jam-centered tarts, the latter dusted over with powdered sugar and spice. They were Hitler's particular favorite.

Hitler sat silently, sucking a lozenge and brooding. His physician, Doctor Morell, was there to taste anything that went onto his plate. The others were silent as well, wondering, no doubt, who would have prevailed among them should Hitler now lie dead. Goering had been officially appointed second in command, but that was years ago. Goering loved toy soldiers and animals, the latter so much that he had framed a law providing six months in jail for anyone removing the legs from frogs before they were painlessly killed. Now Goering's toys were broken, his airplanes all smashed. Then there was Hitler's secretary, Martin Bormann, who was always ready with the right words. Now, as usual, he was the first to speak. "Mein Fuehrer, this fearful attempt on your life has fused the country together. Sabotage by irresponsible soldiers has now become unthinkable. The party will turn with relief to its tasks and undertake them with new energy."

Not to be outdone, Ribbentrop, the Foreign Minister, stood up and offered a toast in camomile tea. "To our blessed Fuehrer, guarded and guided by Divine Providence."

Doenitz, First Admiral of the Navy, was next on his feet. "Please, gentlemen. Three times, *Sieg Heil*. Our Fuehrer, Adolf Hitler . . . *Sieg Heil! Sieg Heil! Sieg Heil!*" The voices gathered volume with each repetition.

Hitler pressed a strawberry tart into his mouth. For an instant it looked as though he were hemorrhaging.

Fish-eyed and worried, Mussolini looked from one face to another. He mouthed *Sieg Heil's* as he had once mouthed *Hail Mary's*. "Thank God for Providence," from Goering. "Thank God for Providence," echoed Keitel. Mussolini had come hoping for an army to liberate Italy, or, short of that, for a promise that Italian workers in Germany might be allowed to go home. He found himself in a cage full of raving parrots who clamored to stuff the Fuehrer's good ear with personal affidavits.

"Mein Fuehrer," declared Admiral Doenitz, "my sailors want you to know this—that they will fight on until final victory or death. Now that the rotten generals have been overturned, the fortress of Britain will fall."

"Not all generals, please," interjected Keitel. "After all!"

Von Ribbentrop outshouted them. "Mein Fuehrer, after today, which brings an end to these traitors and warmongers, things will change. My diplomats in the Balkans will seize the advantage in your behalf."

Then Goering heaved himself to his feet. "Now at last we know why our courageous armies retire in the east. The generals have betrayed them. Now my invincible Hermann Goering Division will drive the Russians back."

"And where is your air force?" sneered Doenitz. "Destroyed."

"At least my pilots had the courage to go out and fight," Goering replied. "How many submarines remain? And you, Ribbentrop. What a fine muck you've made of things as a diplomat. You're a fine champagne salesman."

Von Ribbentrop was red faced as a cockerel. "Meyer!" he shrieked. "Meyer! I'm calling you Meyer. Where are your planes, Meyer, when Berlin is being bombed? Where are they when Hamburg's in flames?"

They screamed at one another like courting cats until Goering advanced ponderously round the tea and cakes, brandishing his field marshal's baton. Ribbentrop backed off, still shouting, "I am the Foreign Minister and my name is *von* Ribbentrop!"

Hitler sat impassive through it all. Occasionally he sucked at a pink pastille, a mixture of strychnine and belladonna which

Von Ribbentrop with Hitler

Doctor Morell had prescribed for his nerves. Mussolini said not a word, watching like a child at a circus when the tigers had broken from their cages. And Himmler, the most dangerous tiger of all, wasn't even there. What if he was behind it all, the Judas absent from the feast?

"Please, gentlemen, try to calm yourselves. Think of the impression you're making." It was Jodl, as usual trying to keep the affair from totally foundering. He failed in his hopes of achieving a pleasant tea party, but he helped shift the focus of frenzy to its ultimate center, Hitler. Casually observed, Hitler might have seemed to preserve throughout a glacial calm. Only those most familiar with his moods recognized his calm as that of a well-fired boiler, needing only a touch on a valve to release a shriek of steam.

Martin Bormann provided the impetus by observing that it was almost the tenth anniversary of the crushing of another alleged plot against Hitler, the 1934 purge of the Storm Troopers. Hitler had just filled his mouth with a cream puff, but his reaction was immediate. Though his lips could not immediately shout, his eyes did. They were the destructive eyes of a willful child. He surged to his feet, struggling to speak. The torrent, when it came, overwhelmed the gathering. "I will smash and destroy these criminals who have presumed to stand in the way of Providence and myself. They may think Germany is an apple to be eaten, but we have found them out! These worms working from inside . . . these foul traitors to their own kind . . . they deserve nothing but ignominious death. And I shall give it to them!" His voice climbed toward an emotional pitch of rhetoric and menace. "This time the full measure will be paid by all who are involved, and by their families!"

As the rain beat against the windows, the voice raved on, and the white-clad SS waiters circulated with teapots and sweets among the gaping worshippers. Mussolini sat huddled and frozen. Marshal Graziani tried to engage Keitel in a whispered discussion, without success. Hitler had to unwind himself. He, no more than any of the others, could have forced a stop. For a full half-hour Hitler dwelt on the exquisite details of revenge. One wave of emotion after another passed over his face and left him finally out of words, panting like a dog.

Mussolini sat up, startled by the jarring silence. The tea party was over. Though Keitel clapped his hands for service and the waiters circulated, the cakes sagged in the sweltering damp heat and the strawberry-studded icing began to slide.

Not until they were returning to his train did Mussolini work up enough courage to mention his problems: his workers in Germany, the demoralizing fall of Rome to the American army, and the spreading partisan menace in the north. Hitler gave him back words. He foretold missiles five times more devastating than the V-1 rockets; victories everywhere with new, loyal leadership. "Varus lost his legions in Germany. Now Germany will give them back," Hitler pledged. "You will lead them in triumph, like Garibaldi." Il Duce had once thought of himself as Garibaldi, but now the steel had gone out of him. There wasn't any point in putting him on his feet; he'd just fall down again. The glittering eyes did not revive him as they once had, and he boarded his train embarrassed, depressed and sadly convinced that history would one day record that he had been ill-used.

"I know that I can depend on you, Duce, and I beg you to believe me when I say that I regard you as my best and possibly only friend left in the world. Take care." These were Hitler's last words before the train pulled away, its doors and windows sealed. The Fuehrer returned through the rain to his bunker. There he was briefly alone with his dog, Blondi, to whom he confided affectionately, "You're worth more than all the others put together. At least you're true to me and understand me."

The coin, of which self-pity is one face with vengeance on the other, was already in capable hands. The little clubfooted Minister of Propaganda, Joseph Goebbels, was the only man Hitler could trust in Berlin. Of course he should have been the first Nazi in the city shot by the conspirators, but they were merciful men imagining a better world. They shed no blood once the bomb had exploded. This was a fatal weakness. Another defect was more military: their trust in the immediate response down the chain of command. If specific orders were ever given for Goebbels' arrest, they had not been set in motion by 5:30 P.M. when Goebbels telephoned East Prussia. They had not been effected half an hour later when an SS bodyguard, responding instantly to Goebbels' call, arrived in force from Lichterfelde to protect him. Unlike the rebels, Goebbels took instant advantage of all the technical aids available. The radio was of first importance and, while the conspirators muddled orders and counter-orders, he moved to keep the *Deutschlandsender* in Nazi hands.

Another curious omission on the part of the conspirators had been to leave their entire military force in the hands of twenty-seven-year-old Major Remer, who was simply under orders and possessed no knowledge that he was acting against the state. Within an hour, Goebbels had located Remer and by seven o'clock the major stood, awed and suspicious, in his office. A lightning call was placed to Hitler, who had decorated Major Remer only weeks before. Once that voice had been heard, there was no mistaking it, and Remer snapped to immediate attention. Another source of physical aid would fail the conspirators hours later when Colonel Mueller, returning to the infantry school at Doeberitz, would be resisted by his junior officers who knew all about the plot.

As the tide turned, defections from the ranks of the conspiracy were quick to hasten its demise. Field Marshal von Witzleben had gone off early in a rage. Count Helldorf of the Berlin police began covering his tracks. Ironically, Major General Stieff, who had been chewing his nails for over a year, was the one who ordered the signal distribution center to process no more messages signed by Witzleben. General Thiele, who had sent out the news of the explosion, thereby triggering *Valkyrie,* began cutting off orders from the conspirators to the armies in the field. With rare exceptions, only the hard core of dedicated men at the Bendlerstrasse held true to their commitments. Small wonder that officers called upon in distant cities to arrest the SS hesitated. In Hamburg the Nazi Gauleiter, Karl Kaufmann, and the Army district commander were close friends, and they spent the evening joking about who should arrest whom. General Schaal, the military commander in the Bohemia-Moravia area, was sipping a beer when the order came to arrest SS officers. But this was hostile territory, full of guerrillas, and he dared not risk open war with the SS. So, for very good reasons, he delayed.

Few of those who vacillated or tried to cover their trails were successful. Count Helldorf, who arrived voluntarily at Goebbels' office pretending to seek information about the disturbance, found himself summarily locked in the music room. General Fromm came as well. Goebbels received him with his feet propped up on a bronze bust of Hitler. "Well, General. So Stauffenberg is dead. What a man! It's almost too bad about him.

What icy determination, what a brain. What an iron will. It's unbelievable that a man of his calibre was surrounded by such donkeys."

"I quite agree, Herr Minister."

"You do, Fromm? You know, you're included in that observation. Really, Fromm, why such a hell of a hurry to put inconvenient witnesses underground?"

Between the execution and the burial of the leading conspirators there had only been time enough for a personnel truck to carry the bodies to the nearest cemetery. Finding the gate locked, the driver and the sergeant in charge had routed the sexton out of a nearby church, opened the gate, and buried the five bodies by night: a general, two colonels, a lieutenant and one civilian. The sexton had seen that much. He'd been told to expect as

Josef Goebbels addressing a meeting

many as thirty more bodies before dawn. They did not arrive. The Gestapo had intervened, wanting living witnesses. At dawn they even sent around a detail of SS who retrieved the buried dead, had them officially photographed, cremated, and their ashes strewn.

Not until Stauffenberg lay temporarily buried did Hitler return from the dead for millions of Germans. For hours the radio had been announcing, then postponing, his speech between outbursts of Wagnerian music. Finally, at 1 A.M. on the morning of July 21, Hans Fritzsche, Hitler's chief radio spokesman, announced, "The Fuehrer speaks!"

Then Hitler's deep and vibrant fury spouted from radios across the land, chilling and crushing the hopes of a few, reviving and reassuring others. "My comrades, men and women of Germany. If I speak to you this day, it is for two important reasons. In the first place, so that you may hear my voice and be reassured that I am fit and unhurt; and in the second place, that you may learn the details of an atrocity without equal in German history. A tiny band of ambitious, ruthless and criminally stupid Army officers conspired to destroy me and along with me the staff of soldiers who are loyal to the *Wehrmacht*. The bomb, which was left by a Colonel Count von Stauffenberg, burst near my right side. It critically injured some of my colleagues, one of whom has since died. But I myself am entirely well.

"The band of assassins is, as you must realize, small. It has nothing to do with our military forces and is detached from your Army. It is a tiny group of criminals which even now is being mercilessly exterminated." So Hitler condemned and sentenced them before the German people with the implacable malice of an insect.

Five thousand were to die, the first and perhaps most fortunate by their own hands. General Tresckow, far off in Russia, received the news of the failure and resigned himself immediately to suicide. His aide, Schlabrendorff, argued with him throughout the night.

"Everyone will turn against us and abuse us," Tresckow told him, "but my belief remains unbroken. We did right. Presently I shall stand before God answering for what I did. My conscience is clear for my stand against Hitler. Schlabrendorff, do you recall how God promised Abraham to spare Sodom should ten just men be found there? Perhaps Germany will be spared for what we have tried to do. We can't complain. When we joined this resistance, it was like putting on the Shirt of Nessus, and we are worth as much as the beliefs for which we give up our lives." This at least is how Schlabrendorff recorded the general's last remarks. With the dawn, Tresckow drove to the Twenty-Sixth Rifle Division. With a pistol and a hand grenade, he walked toward the Russian lines. He could have surrendered, but his despair was too great for that. Discharging his pistol to give the illusion of dying in combat, he then held the grenade to his body and drew the pin.

Not long after that, Field Marshal Guenther von Kluge, in whom Tresckow had created vacillation but not conviction, was relieved of his command in France and recalled to Germany. On August 19, he stopped his staff car for a picnic near Verdun. There he wrote as follows: "Mein Fuehrer, I have always esteemed your greatness, your iron will to sustain yourself and National Socialism. You have fought a brave fight. Now show yourself great enough to end this hopeless struggle. I leave you, Mein Fuehrer, as one with more loyalty than you imagine." With this last salute, Field Marshal Kluge took poison and died.

Two months later, poison terminated the career of another field marshal. Erwin Rommel, recovering at home from his wounds, was visited by the SS and told he had the choice of poison or public trial which would extend retribution to his family. He drove off with the SS in their little green car and was later reported dead of his wounds in the Army Reserve Hospital at Ulm. A state funeral was ordered, at which Field Marshal von Rundstedt intoned the eulogy, concluding, "His heart belonged to the Fuehrer."

Another to attempt suicide was General Stuelpnagel. He had

lived to see twelve hundred key men of the Gestapo and SS put under arrest in Paris; lived to see his brilliant work undone when the plot failed in Berlin. He might have fled to the Allied lines. He had the time and the means, but instead he drove toward Germany. Along the way he stopped and said that he wished to walk alone. While his driver waited dutifully by the car, Stuelpnagel pressed a pistol to his head. He succeeded only in blinding himself, was carried unconscious to a Verdun hospital, revived, and made to stand trial. Denying nothing, he was hanged at Ploetzensee on August 29.

These trials went on as long as the war lasted, as did the hangings. Over four hundred detectives under Himmler were required to investigate the men to whom Hitler had referred as a small clique. The pattern was set by the officers' trial of August 7 and 8. Among those accused at this early date were General Hoepner, who had refused Fromm's offer of honorable suicide the night of the conspiracy, Frotiz von der Schulenburg, Deputy Police President of Berlin, his chief, Heinrich Wolf von Helldorf, and Field Marshal von Witzleben. The point was not to establish justice but to humiliate. The accused were given oversized civilian clothes, deprived of belts and artificial teeth, then tongue-lashed by Hitler's merciless Robespierre, Judge Roland Freisler of the Peoples' Court. Death sentences were virtually automatic and execution was swift at Ploetzensee prison. Under huge klieg lights with newsreel cameras grinding, the handcuffed prisoners were hung from meat hooks.

With the active conspirators disposed of, the net of retribution spread wider to include those who had only talked and sympathized. Helmuth von Moltke, a legal advisor to the *Abwehr* and spiritual head of the nonviolent intellectual group called the Kreisau Circle, was dragged from the jail cell where he had languished for nearly two years, and executed. Another to die out of hand, shot down by the SS when the Allied armies drew too close in the spring of 1945, was Dietrich Bonhoeffer, Germany's most promising young theologian, who had given spiritual support to the resistance. Doctor Carl Goerdeler, the conspiracy's civilian gadfly and candidate for Chancellor, hid successfully among friends for several weeks, but was finally captured, tried, and condemned. He would write from prison: "I beg the world to take our martyrs' death as penance for the German people." It was too much to ask, of course, but it was sincerely said by a man who had not lost his honor. Executed at the same time was Julius Leber, who had once been Stauffenberg's preference for Chancellor. Writing less extravagantly, he left this final message: "For so good and just a cause, the cost of one's own life is a fair price."

Condemned for cowardice and a guilty mind was Colonel General Fritz Fromm. He would not hang until March, 1945. His manipulations had extended his life by half a year. Just before the greased trap opened beneath his feet, he was heard to pledge final loyalty to the Fuehrer.

Field Marshal Erwin von Witzleben, on trial

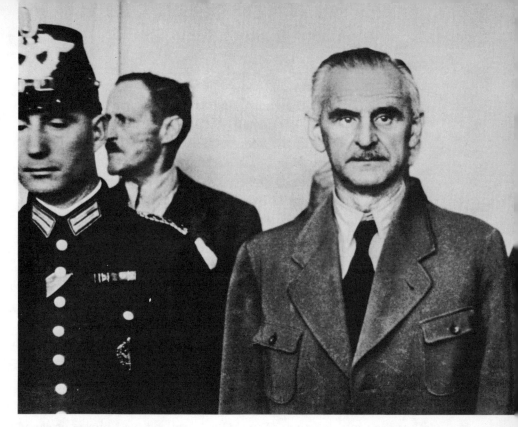

Carl Goerdeler, on trial

Vengeance did not stop with those guilty in mind or word. It reached out to the innocent, under the Nazi doctrine of guilt by association, which imagined guilt extending through bonds of blood and marriage. Among others, Stauffenberg's wife, Nina, and his children were arrested and sent to the concentration camp at Bad Sachsa. There Nina gave birth to her fifth child, whose last name, along with all the others, was changed to "Meister." All survived the war and have resumed their own name with the honor it now bears.

There were other survivors. Hans Berndt Gisevius, who had come from Switzerland to take part in the coup, made his way safely back there. Two of the soldiers who were brought from the Russian front to explode the bomb in Hitler's arms survived.

Captain Ewald von Kleist was arrested along with his father.

"It will be easier for me to submit to the death penalty than for you to inflict it," the father had said at his trial, and he went to his death like a gentleman. Defeat caught up with Germany before it could kill the son. Axel von dem Bussche, who had returned to the front and lost his leg, was never under suspicion. In fact, while in the hospital he received a hamper of food with a gold embossed card, "From your grateful Fuehrer."

Elisabeth Struenck, who with her husband had sheltered so many conspiratorial meetings at Nuernbergerstrasse 31, outlived the hangman. Her husband did not. But the closest brush with death came to Major Fabian von Schlabrendorff, Tresckow's aide, who had once placed a bomb aboard Hitler's airplane. Arrested and brought to trial, he was actually being examined by Judge Freisler, when the courthouse was struck by Allied bombs. Freisler died in the rubble and the trial records were destroyed. Tried again, Schlabrendorff was acquitted, but was turned over to the SS for disposal. A firing squad rather than hanging was to have been the only distinction between conviction and acquittal, but the rapid advance of the Allied armies saved him as it saved so many.

At this point, the pendulum had swung. It was time for Hitler and his court to perish. Il Duce set the pattern. On April 28, 1945, Mussolini and his mistress, Clara Petacci, were shot by partisans in the hamlet of Mezzagra. For a whole day their remains hung head down from the roof of a gas station in Milan's Piazza Loreto.

Hitler would survive them by barely two days. In the last six months he had become a shuffling, ashen old man. He had lost control of the left side of his body. A guard had to thrust a chair under him when he tried to sit. Devious plots seemed baked into every strawberry tart. He sipped his tea fearfully and occasionally vomited without apparent reason. The war was no longer his to control. He directed phantom armies, turning more and more from talk of conquest and revenge to anecdotes about his dogs and his diets and complaints about the wicked foolishness of a world that did not appreciate him.

He was supposed to leave Berlin on April 20, 1945, his fifty-sixth birthday, and yet he hesitated, imagining that his SS General Obergruppenfuehrer Steiner would sweep away the oncoming Russian army. The encounter never took place, for the Russians were already in the city of Berlin. A six-pointed cloth Star of David was the best selling item on the Berlin black market when, on April 30, Hitler decided to die. What had begun with the *Horst Wessel Lied* expired to the gloomy strains of Bruckner's Seventh Symphony. As it played over Berlin radio with the announcement of Hitler's passing, some Germans who still had radios, wept for their Fuehrer.

Joseph Goebbels, his wife and children, died together when Hitler died. Himmler of the flaccid face and slender womanly hands tried to escape, but was taken by British troops near

Major Fabian von Schlabrendorff, on trial

Teufels Moor, "The Devil's Moor." Identified, he forced a cyanide pill between his teeth before his guards could stop him. Thus he, too, cheated the Allied judges at Nuremberg. Reich Marshal Goering obtained poison. Keitel and Jodl, with their big ears and gentle grandfatherly faces, were hung. In the tumult of collapse, one death went almost unrecorded. Major Ernst Remer, who had played so great a part in the conspiracy's failure, though promoted to colonel, could find nothing more to live for. He died with the barrel of a pistol clenched between his teeth.

The holocaust of dying did not end there. It extended even to the pitiful army of anti-communist Russian volunteers raised by Stauffenberg in 1942. Most of these units were captured by the western allies toward the end of the war. The Russians demanded them back. The British, in most cases, declared them "Poles" and in time they became sad-faced English farmers. The Americans, less long at war, less aware, perhaps, of its realities, handed them over to the Soviet government. Most were executed.

Even in this, the final result of Stauffenberg's efforts was death. He was, if measured by results, a complete failure. A childish "telephone *Putsch*," Goebbels called the plot, and in a sense he was correct. As soon as the facts were known, the New York *Herald Tribune* editorialized in the summer of 1944, "Let the generals kill the corporal or vice-versa; both would suit us." Two years later, the Sunday edition of *The New York Times* could say in all seriousness, "It is just as well that the attempt did fail. Had it succeeded, the army officers who planned it would have sought peace at once and might have saved the German Army." True. Perhaps, also, the old World War One myth that Germany had lost because of a "stab in the back" might have been revived. But such views disregard the millions of men, women and children who died on the battlefields, under bombs and in concentration camps during those last nine months of war. Not until July 20, 1959, was official notice taken of the conspiracy. Then it was by the West German army in this statement: "The act of July 20, 1944—an act directed against

Commemorative stamps issued July 20, 1964, by the West German Federal Republic; TOP, LEFT TO RIGHT: *Sophie Scholl, Ludwig Beck, Helmuth von Moltke;* BOTTOM, LEFT TO RIGHT: *Dietrich Bonhoeffer, Carl Goerdeler, Claus von Stauffenberg.*

wrong and slavery—is a shining light in Germany's darkest hour."

Only a salute to failure? They were not natural revolutionaries, these conscience-pricked soldiers. They had little taste for blood, and yet one wonders. If Rommel had not been wounded . . . if Kluge had acted decisively . . . pure speculation. In measurable terms, the plot was worse than failure. It left Germany in more fanatic hands than ever before, and bled the land of its most promising leaders for the postwar years. Could he have foreseen this, would Stauffenberg have resigned himself? Would he have accepted life as it was and waited out defeat? Undoubtedly not. There was something invincible inside him, an infusion of greatness in simplicity, which enabled him to challenge a dictatorship based on mass support and armed for total war. He had come into this drama only at the last act. He had rapidly taken charge, carrying new determination and courage to the flagging opposition, which was discouraged and broken by arrests. When resolution failed, he overcame the hesitancy of some and the scruples of a few. At Army headquarters in Berlin as well as in East Prussia, he was the one force that moved, drawing the conspiracy behind him. This quality is all the more incredible when his physical disabilities are tallied up. These would have been sufficient to turn lesser men into street beggars, but he remained the one-eyed head and three-fingered hand of the adventure, failing perhaps only because he could not be in two places at the same time. Some, envying his winning personality and his sure step, might suggest that his ruined body had brought on a reckless indifference to living, even a pre-disposition for martyrdom. This was not so. To the end, he retained a taste for life and a gift for laughter, but he chose, none-theless and without illusion, the hard and lonely path. In the darkness of defeat and dishonor, he became for a short time the brightest star of human decency to flicker over Germany. At the end, he was alone, like every man who has ever tried to give himself to all men. His life was not wasted. It was a triumph, and his memory will shine on as long as there are human tears, as long as man has hope and courage, as long as there remain the seeds of Hitler and his kind in the blood, and that may well be forever.

A SHORT GLOSSARY

Abwehr	Intelligence Bureau; also a center of the conspiracy.
Deutschlandsender	Berlin Radio
Gestapo	Short form of *Geheime Staatspolizei,* or Secret State Police.
Luftwaffe	Air Force
OKW	Initials for *Oberkommando der Wehrmacht,* or High Command of the Armed Forces.
SA	Initials for *Sturmabteilung,* or Storm Troopers, also known as Brownshirts. Early strong-arm squads of the Nazi Party.
SS	Initials for *Schutzstaffel,* or Bodyguard. Originally the Fuehrer's bodyguard, later elite armed branch of the Nazi Party, in charge of police power and concentration camps throughout the Reich.
SD	Initials for *Sicherheitsdienst,* or Security Service. SS and Gestapo division responsible for general surveillance and liquidation of population groups throughout the Reich.
Wehrmacht	Literally, Armed Forces, but usually referring to the Army.

BIBLIOGRAPHY

Stauffenberg

FINKER, KURT, *Stauffenberg,* Union Verlag Berlin, DDR, 1970.

KRAMARZ, JOACHIM, *Stauffenberg, Macmillan Co.,* New York, 1967.

MUELLER, CHRISTIAN, *Oberst I. G. Stauffenberg,* Droste Verlag, Duesseldorf, DBR, 1972.

Conspiracy

DEUTSCH, HAROLD CHARLES, *The Conspiracy Against Hitler in the Twilight War,* University of Minnesota Press, Minneapolis, 1968.

DONOHOE, JAMES, *Hitler's Conservative Opponents in Bavaria 1930-1945,* E. J. Brill, Netherlands, 1961.

FITZGIBBON, CONSTANTINE, *20 July,* W. W. Norton and Co., Inc., New York, 1956.

GOERLITZ, WALTER, *History of the German General Staff,* Praeger, New York, 1953.

MANVELL, ROGER, and FRAENKEL, HEINRICH, *The Canaris Conspiracy,* David McKay Co., New York, 1969.

MANVELL, ROGER, and FRAENKEL, HEINRICH, *The Men Who Tried to Kill Hitler,* Coward, McCann, New York, 1964.

PRITTIE, TERENCE, *Germans Against Hitler,* Little, Brown and Co., Boston, 1964.

SCHLABRENDORFF, FABIAN VON, *The Secret War Against Hitler,* Pilman, New York, 1965.

SCHOLL, INGE, *Six Against Tyranny,* John Murray, London, 1955.

Germany—World War Two

ALLEN, WILLIAM SHERIDAN, *The Nazi Seizure of Power,* Quadrangle Books, Chicago, 1965.

BLUMENSON, MARTIN, *Kasserine Pass,* Houghton Mifflin, Boston 1966.

BRAUTIGAN, RICHARD, *Rommel Drives On Deep Into Egypt,* Delta, New York, 1970.

BRYANT, ARTHUR, *The Turn of the Tide, 1939-43,* Doubleday, Garden City, New York, 1957.

CARRELL, PAUL, *Invasion—They're Coming,* E. P. Dutton and Co., New York, 1962.

CARRELL, PAUL, *Hitler Moves East, 1941-43,* Little, Brown and Co., Boston, 1965.

CRANKSHAW, EDWARD, *Gestapo,* Pyramid Books, New York, Viking Press, New York, 1956.

DEAKIN, FREDERICK WILLIAM, *The Brutal Friendship,* Harper and Row, New York, 1962.

GRUNBERGER, RICHARD, *The 12 Year Reich,* Holt, Rinehart and Winston, New York, 1971.

HART, B. H. LIDDELL (Editor), *The Rommel Papers,* Harcourt Brace and Co., New York, 1953.

HILL, RUSSELL, *Desert War,* Alfred A. Knopf, New York, 1942.

MOOREHEAD, ALAN, *The March to Tunis,* Harper and Row, New York, 1965.

NYISZLI, MIKLOS, *Auschwitz,* Fawcett Pub. Inc., Greenwich, Conn., 1960.

RECK-MALLEYEWEN, FRITZ PERCY, *Diary of a Man in Despair,* Macmillan, New York, 1970.

SHIRER, WILLIAM, *The Rise and Fall of the Third Reich,* Simon and Schuster, New York, 1959.

SPEER, ALBERT, *Inside the Third Reich,* Macmillan Co., New York, 1970.

TREVOR-ROPER, H. R., *The Last Days of Hitler,* Macmillan Co., New York, 1947.

VOGT, HANNAH, *The Burden of Guilt,* Oxford Univ. Press, New York, 1964.

WERTH, ALEXANDER, *Russia at War,* Dutton and Co., New York, 1964.

WHEATON, ELIOT BARULE, *Prelude to Calamity: The Nazi Revolution,* Doubleday, Garden City, New York, 1968.

WHEELER-BENNETT, JOHN, *The Nemesis of Power: The German Army in Politics 1918-1945,* Macmillan Co., New York, 1953.

YOUNG, DESMOND, *Rommel, the Desert Fox,* Harper and Row, New York, 1950.

INDEX

Italicized page numbers refer to illustrations